SPEAKING OUT

SPEAKING OUT

TARA MOSS

A 21ST-CENTURY HANDBOOK FOR WOMEN & GIRLS

HarperCollins*Publishers*

HarperCollins_Publishers_

First published in Australia in 2016
by HarperCollins_Publishers_ Australia Pty Limited
ABN 36 009 913 517
harpercollins.com.au

HarperCollins_Publishers_
Level 13, 201 Elizabeth Street, Sydney NSW 2000, Australia
Unit D1, 63 Apollo Drive, Rosedale, Auckland 0632, New Zealand
A 53, Sector 57, Noida, UP, India
1 London Bridge Street, London SE1 9GF, United Kingdom
2 Bloor Street East, 20th floor, Toronto, Ontario M4W 1A8, Canada
195 Broadway, New York, NY 10007, USA

National Library of Australia Cataloguing-in-Publication data:

Moss, Tara, author.
  Speaking out : a 21st-century handbook for women and girls /
Tara Moss.
  ISBN: 978 1 4607 5133 6 (hardback)
  ISBN: 978 1 4607 0601 5 (ebook)
  Public speaking for women.
  Self-confidence.
  Self-presentation.
808.51082

Cover design by Hazel Lam, HarperCollins Design Studio, and Tara Moss, based
on a concept by Tara Moss
Internal design by Hazel Lam, HarperCollins Design Studio
Photography by Steve Baccon
Make-up by Rachel Montgomery
Hair by Paula Hibbard
Typeset in ITC Caslon 224 and Archer by Kirby Jones
Printed and bound in Australia by Griffin Press
The papers used by HarperCollins in the manufacture of this book are a natural,
recyclable product made from wood grown in sustainable plantation forests.
The fibre source and manufacturing processes meet recognised international
environmental standards, and carry certification.

To all the women who got us here

Antifeminist Bingo card reproduced with kind permission from Sarah Grey; Extract from *Harvard Study on Women's Experiences at Harvard Law School* reproduced with kind permission from Adam Neufeld; Extract from *Lawstuff* website reproduced with kind permission from Lawstuff; Extract from *Q&A* reproduced with kind permission from the Australian Broadcasting Corporation; Information on vicarious trauma reproduced with kind permission from Rape & Domestic Violence Services Australia; Information on voice training included with kind permission from Lucy Cornell, Voice Coach; Personal stories of survival included with kind permission of Van Badham, Rosie Batty, Carly Findlay, Amy Gray, Amanda Palmer, Karen Pickering, Natasha Stott Despoja, Miranda Tapsell, Saba Vasefi and Mariam Veiszadeh.

The author gratefully acknowledges the permission to reproduce copyright material in this book. Every effort has been made to trace and acknowledge copyright. Where the attempt has been unsuccessful, the author would be pleased to hear from the copyright holder to rectify any omission or error in a future reprint.

Contents

...

To Speak is to be Human

...

Having a voice is part of what makes us human, and freedom of speech – being allowed to use our voice – is one primary sign of living in a 'free' society. As social animals, communication is a central part of being human. Speaking and being heard is a vital acknowledgment of both our status as fellow beings worthy of being heard and our similarities, and for this reason many a philosopher has contemplated just how differently we might treat animals if they were able to speak our language – or we theirs. Language connects us. Our voices connect us. When we are silent or unheard our ideals and perspectives, our needs, our pain, and our struggles remain unknown or unacknowledged; and often for this reason, unchanged.

Despite the relative freedom we enjoy in the 'West' (a term which commonly includes Australia and New Zealand, quite 'East') and new opportunities to speak out, including on digital platforms and social media, commenting on a subject in the public sphere is not always easy or simple. There are specific challenges that face many segments of the population in speaking out and being heard, or surviving the process. These include challenges relating to gender, race, sexual orientation, class, culture and disability. In this book I aim to examine the challenges posed by gender – specifically those facing women and girls – the external obstacles of silencing, dismissals, bullying and threats of violence, and the internal challenges of crises of confidence, and knowing just how and when to speak out.

Why write this book? Because the world has become more receptive to the voices of women in recent decades and at the same time it has become more violently opposed to women's voices. Today, when less than one out of every four people we hear from or about is female, this fact bears examination. Just what are women experiencing when they speak out? If you want to be heard, what strategies work? This book attempts to answer some of those questions, and more.

Technology has created exciting new opportunities to speak out. A lot of our interaction with the world, including private communications and public 'speaking out', is now performed digitally, from simple social-media communications or instant messages to blogs and other electronic publishing. Technology has provided new spaces for people to respond, sometimes politely and constructively, sometimes savagely, with women emerging as particular targets of online harassment and abuse, in gendered and even violently sexualised ways. As many women like myself know all too well, having an opinion as a woman online now comes with gendered abuse, almost as an expectation. Speak out against rape and murder … get rape and death threats. Speak out against inequality and have your 'f*ckability' rating assessed by trolls, who presumably think this is the only use for a woman.

Recognising the common language and methods used by trolls and abusers does not necessarily remove these unpleasant realities but it does provide perspective, and helpful armour. For this reason, *Speaking Out* focuses on several forms of speaking out, including public speaking and writing, but has a particular focus on online experiences; what can happen and what can be done about it, with advice from women who have been there.

* * *

This book is divided into three parts, with the aim of answering the basic questions: WHY should I speak out? HOW do I speak out? And finally, WHAT MIGHT I EXPECT when I speak out? Of course, this book can't *really* be categorised so neatly – there's material on WHY and HOW to speak out, and WHAT TO EXPECT in almost every chapter. Broadly speaking, however, the chapters in this book are divided into that framework so that I am able to put my case to you first (arguing your point is important when speaking out, as we will discuss later) before giving tips on how to make your case and how to survive speaking it.

One of my aims is to give practical advice to anyone who feels trepidation about the critics – both the constructive kind and the unconstructive – and the trolls. But another is to build confidence and knowledge through shared experience. Because by retelling our triumphs and failures, and the responses we got along the way, we get a greater sense of strength. By comparing notes, we can learn to recognise and differentiate constructive criticism from the silencing and the trolling, and most importantly, know that we are human and in this together.

This is a twenty-first century guide for speaking out.

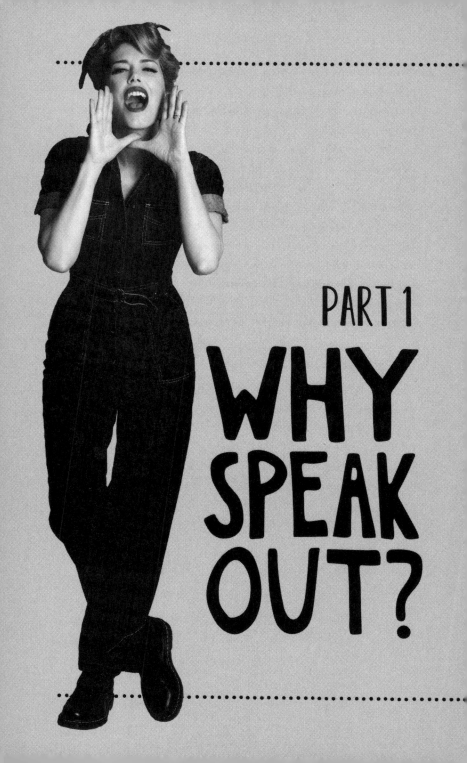

PART 1

WHY SPEAK OUT?

Why do we need more diversity and women's and girl's voices? Why should *you* speak out? It is essential that we understand the basics of why it matters, what common issues arise specifically for women and girls, and what the public playing field, so to speak, currently looks like.

Though not everyone identifies as male or female, it is safe to say that roughly half of the population are female, half male and it is therefore notable that despite this fairly even distribution of the sexes throughout the world, the participation in public life and in the corridors of power is significantly male-skewed. (And not just any male, as we will discuss. Race, class and other issues factor in.) This disparity is widespread, but is by no means consistent from country to country, nor has it been consistent from age to age. The disproportionate focus, influence and power afforded to one demographic and one sex is not inevitable or natural any more than it has been static from decade to decade. The opportunities afforded to me, and most of the women and girls reading this, are very different than they were 25 years ago, let alone 50 or 100 years ago. The interim has brought social, cultural and political change. The fact that level of inequality *can* change is vital to know, before we get down to some of the methods you might use to prepare to speak out, do it, and survive to do it again.

CHAPTER 1

SHHH

Women talk less?

...

If you want to participate in your community and be heard, you will need to speak out in some way. While this is important for all members of the community, to date, the approximately one-half of the population identified as female has been significantly less often heard than the half that is identified as male.[1]

'Wait a second!' I hear some of you saying. 'Women are *less* often heard?'

I'm sure you've heard the stereotype about how women are more talkative than men, and possibly you even believe it to be true. Perhaps your father or another authority figure used to talk about women's wagging tongues. Perhaps you've heard one of the many charming jokes about women, like: 'Why do men have two heads and women four lips? Because men do all the thinking and women do all the talking.' Perhaps you've come across one of the many proverbs about women's mouthiness: 'Women's tongues are like lambs' tails – always wagging' (English proverb). 'Where there are women and geese, there's noise' (Japanese proverb). 'Foxes are all tail and women are all tongue' (English proverb). 'The woman with active hands and feet, marry her, but the woman with overactive mouth, leave well alone' (Maori proverb).

With so many quips and sayings about women's pronounced prattling, surely there must be some truth to the accusation? And if women are indeed the talkative sex, speaking out should be easier for them, because they do it all the time, right?

Not so fast.

The first thing to point out here is that the stereotype about how women talk more than men does not accord with research. Knowing this is important, because the perception that women's voices are too frequently heard affects the way we listen – or *don't* listen – to women when they speak out.

As well as all the jokes and proverbs, there are a lot of articles written about women's apparently verbose natures. Some even make the scientific-sounding pronouncement that women use 20,000 words per day and their male counterparts just 7000. The *Daily Mail* was among those citing this erroneous claim as fact, in a 2013 article delicately titled 'Sorry to interrupt, dear, but women really do talk more than men (13,000 words a day more to be precise)'. The article asserted that 'now scientists have found the key to explaining why women are the more talkative sex. A study just published suggests that higher levels of the protein are found in the female brain.'[2]

The study in question was one that correlated talkativity with a protein called Foxp2. It did not, however, look at human women and their talkativity at all. It looked at rats and the prevalence of the Foxp2 protein in male rats, which are apparently more 'talkative'. It then tested 10 children and found that among those 10 the girls had more of the Foxp2 protein than the boys.[3] Simon Fisher, one of the Oxford team[4] who first discovered the protein, cautioned against drawing conclusions from a study of such a small number of children, but the *Daily Mail* was unswayed. It even illustrated the article with a cartoon of a man reading a newspaper that proclaimed:

> If even women with considerable public power and influence cop the "Shhhh" when others are watching and recording the exchange, what happens to women with less power?

FEMALES SPEAK 13,000 MORE WORDS A DAY.
Man: Good grief! Is that all?!

It may be surprising, then, to learn that the vast majority of studies to date show that it is actually men who talk more, particularly in mixed-gender settings. And importantly for the context of this book, it is *men* who tend to talk significantly more in *public settings*.

But what about those 20,000 daily words, I hear you say? Where does this 'fact' come from? It turns out that it was distributed via a book titled *The Female Brain* (2006) by Louann Brizendine, a neuropsychiatrist at the University of California San Francisco. The 20,000 versus 7,000 words per day 'statistic' appeared on the dust jacket, and was widely quoted in reviews. A professor of linguistics at the University of Pennsylvania, Mark Liberman, questioned the figures, and Brizendine agreed that it would not appear on future editions. When Liberman sought a further source, he found nothing except for a similar claim in a 1993 marriage guidance pamphlet.[5]

In short, it was one of those stats that was never properly sourced, but conveniently backed up a pre-existing stereotype and spread like wildfire.

As far back as the 1990s, researchers knew the stereotype that women talk more than men was bunkum. In 1993, linguistics researcher Deborah James and social psychologist Janice Drakich reviewed 63 studies about the amount of talk by men and women in various contexts and found that in 61 of the studies men talked more.[6] Peter Kunsmann, Professor of English Philology at the Free University of Berlin, sums this up well when he points out: 'Most studies find that in mixed talks men tend to be more dominating than women.'[7]

Not all women, not all men, not all conversations, but in 61 out of 63 studies men talked more, and they more often show the characteristics of domination. This makes the claim that women talk too much seem particularly curious. As US journalist and author Soraya Chemaly puts it, 'The reality is not that women talk more … but that we want and expect them to talk less.'[8]

Of course, there is some historical context to this idea, as evidenced by numerous texts. In ancient Greece, the writer Plutarch had this advice: 'for married women staying at home silence is becoming'.[9] The Bible, along with other religious texts, also suggests strongly that for women, remaining silent is best. According to 1 Timothy 2:11–12: 'A woman should learn in quietness and full submission. I do not permit a woman to teach or to assume authority over a man; she must be quiet.' And in 1 Corinthians 14:34: 'Women should remain silent in the churches. They are not allowed to speak, but must be in submission, as the law says.'[10]

Fortunately things have changed a lot over the centuries. But the fact that many men (and women) today still expect and want women to talk less – whether they realise it or not – factors into the experiences women have when speaking out.

The Quiet Woman

There is a 400-year-old pub in the village of Earl
Sterndale, Derbyshire, named The Quiet Woman,
with a sign outside depicting a female server with no
head, holding a tray carrying beer and food. The pub's
name is said to refer to 'a too talkative woman who was
decapitated as a consequence'.[11] The words at the top of
the sign (from Proverbs 15:1) say 'Soft Words Turneth
Away Wrath'.

Fascinating fact: social conventions didn't exactly
encourage women to drink in pubs until fairly recently,
especially without male chaperones to supervise/
protect them – and such behaviour is still contested
as being 'dangerous', 'unfeminine' etc for women, if
various headlines are to be believed. ('Do you know
what your daughter's doing tonight?'[12] 'College Women:
stop getting drunk,'[13] 'Judge in rape trial warning:
"Conviction rates will not improve until women stop
drinking so heavily"[14] and 'CDC [US Centres for Disease
Control and Prevention] tells fertile women: Don't drink
at all'[15] I mean, how dare an adult woman drink alcohol
and expect not to get raped? How dare a woman of
legal and reproductive age, who isn't pregnant or even
planning to have a baby, have a drink? Doesn't she
know she has a womb?) A certain type of (usually male)
authority has always felt it was best for women to stay
indoors, as evidenced by this anecdote from former
Israeli Prime Minister Golda Meir: 'Once in a Cabinet
we had to deal with the fact that there had been an

outbreak of assaults on women at night. One minister suggested a curfew; women should stay home after dark. I said, "But it's the men who are attacking the women. If there's to be a curfew, let the men stay home, not the women.'"[16]

Between notions of protecting women by keeping them home (where they are ironically at most risk of assault[17]) and the idea that women drinking alcohol is dangerous for them and not for men, women gathering in pubs has tended to be discouraged. In fact, it wasn't until 1982 that women in the UK were finally allowed to spend their money in English pubs without the threat of being legally refused service, after two female Fleet Street journalists won a case against London's El Vino wine bar.[18]

So the eponymous woman depicted on the old sign in her traditional server's dress is most probably mutely serving groups of *men* – while decapitated, which adds another level of discomfort to the scene. I'd say that if the historical account is true, she was murdered not as a consequence of being 'too talkative' but for the crime of being female and having an opinion, in a time when that was still distinctly taboo.

Silencing and interruptions

...

One issue that comes up again and again for the woman who speaks out publicly is a tendency to be patronisingly interrupted, or told to calm down or be silent. Surprisingly, this is true even for women who are in positions of authority, or speaking as experts. CNBC anchor Kelly Evans was told to 'calm down' and was given the 'Shhhh' on live TV when interviewing US senator Rand Paul in 2015. In 2014 Turkish Deputy Prime Minister Bülent Arınç urged women not to laugh in public, in order to 'protect moral values',[19] and in a parliamentary meeting in 2015 he shouted, 'Shush lady, be silent as a woman' to Peoples' Democratic Party deputy Nursel Aydogan.[20] In 2013 then Australian Opposition Leader Tony Abbott told *Guardian* journalist Bridie Jabour to 'calm down' when he didn't like her line of questioning.[21] In 2011, UK PM David Cameron told a (female) MP to 'Calm down, dear' during question time.[22] In 2015 Australian senator Penny Wong was told by Senator George Brandis during parliamentary question time that she was 'becoming hysterical' and needed to calm down. She later joked on Twitter: 'After being called shrill and hysterical by George Brandis, I'm off to my office for a cup of tea, a Bex and a lie down.'[23]

Speaking of tea, Peta Credlin, the Chief of Staff to former PM Tony Abbott, said after 16 years in politics in Australia, 'Nine times out of 10, here and overseas, I am the only woman. And people ask me to get the cup of tea.'[24] If that isn't another form of 'Shhhh' – and one that literally requires a woman to dismiss herself from the room unless she flatly refuses – I don't know what is.

In 2015 US presidential candidate Hillary Clinton was 'told to stop shouting about gun violence', and responded, 'I'm not shouting. It's just when women talk, people think we're shouting.'[25] And a 2012 Yale University study looking at male and female US senators found a strong positive relationship between power and volubility in the men, with no such link in the women. Instead, the women were found to 'incur backlash as a result of talking more than others – an effect that is observed among both male and female perceivers'. In other words, the male senators were rewarded for speaking out, as it reinforced the sense of their power and importance. Women knew they were more likely to be 'rewarded' with backlash and did not speak as much.[26] You can see how this might affect the functioning of democracy.

On a more violent note, in 2015 Northern Territory Attorney-General John Elferink, then a White Ribbon Ambassador (a male-led organisation protesting violence against women), interrupted MP Natasha Fyles several times and told the parliament: 'I'm really tempted to give her a slap right now ... figuratively speaking.'[27] Also in 2015, former Australian cricketer Merv Hughes, on the reality show *I'm a Celebrity ... Get Me Out of Here!*, told a female contestant who asked him to help with cooking dinner, 'Sit down, woman ... shut up or I'll chop your head off with this machete'[28] – an image with unfortunate echoes of the Quiet Woman pub decapitation story (see box, **The Quiet Woman**, on pages 20 to 21).

These recent high-profile examples matter because they demonstrate that no woman is immune to this particular form of male dismissal. If even women with considerable public power and influence cop the 'Shhhh' when others are watching and recording the exchange, what happens to women with less power? And what happens when other parliamentarians or millions of TV viewers aren't watching? These recorded instances represent the tip of the iceberg of what is still a surprisingly widespread phenomenon – experienced by women far from the cameras, in boardrooms, public meetings, businesses, schools and homes.

Multiple studies of interactions between doctors and patients, for instance, suggest female doctors are interrupted by patients more often than male doctors. One study from 1984 concluded that women were interrupted fully twice as often as men,[29] though one hopes things have improved at least a little since then. Other studies assert that all doctors, male and female, interrupt female patients more often than male patients.[30] Female doctors are less likely to interrupt patients than male doctors,[31] which is consistent with the observation that women in general tend to speak over others less frequently.

I have seen this phenomenon many times in public talks to promote my books. The most striking example would be my tour for *The Fictional Woman* in 2014, during which I spoke to perhaps 100 separate audiences across five Australian States over a period of several months. Because the book deals with feminist issues – the title being something of a giveaway – the audiences were often over 90% female. But from universities to local book shops, in all but one talk, the first audience member to speak during question time was male. This was true even where there happened to be 199 women and one man.

I am hardly alone in perceiving this trend. 'I have observed this pattern at my own lectures, which concern issues of direct relevance to women. Regardless of the proportion of women and men in the audience, men almost invariably ask the first question, more questions, and longer questions', writes Dr Deborah Tannen (University Professor and Professor of Linguistics at Georgetown University).[32] One Harvard study concluded that, in mixed-gender educational settings, 'Compared with female students, men were 64% more likely to speak three or more times in a class, and 144% more likely to volunteer three or more comments.'[33]

Why are women less likely to raise their hands in public forums? Why are so many men less hesitant about getting up and speaking, even when the topic relates to the experiences of women? If it is a matter of confidence, why are women less confident than men even when the topic is something they would be more likely to know about? Most agree that social conditioning plays a strong role in these patterns, and is something we as individuals can choose to consciously address and change.

What do you do if you get the 'Shhhh'?

- Suggest the offender might want to calm themselves and focus. The 'Shhhh' is a sure-fire sign that the offender feels they have control of the conversation, and is attempting to wrest it back by being patronising, to show that they have the authority and control (see **Chapter 7: How to Recognise a Diversion**). They don't. You deserve to share the floor. Say what you have to say.
- Suggest that if they listen they might just learn something.
- Sometimes the best response is a good incredulous stare, perhaps even a raised brow. Many of the world's top woman commentators, politicians and experts have a great knack for this, no doubt developed over years of experience.

The media and storytelling

...

Naturally this pattern of male-dominated conversation carries over into participation in the media. In a 2010 study, 1281 newspapers, television and radio stations were monitored in 108 countries. The review covered 16,734 news items, 20,769 news personnel (announcers, presenters and reporters), and 35,543 news subjects. It found that only 24% of the people heard or read about in print, radio and television news are female. That means more than three-quarters of those in the news are male.[34]

In Australia we see a breakdown like this across national and commercial broadcasters:

- Television presenters: female 24 (22%), male 86 (78%)
- Television reporters: female 14 (25%), male 43 (75%)
- Radio presenters: female 23 (34%), male 45 (66%)
- Radio reporters: female 5 (42%), male 7 (58%).[35]

Crucially, the 24% global average in 2010 is up from just 17% in 1995. Things are changing – though there is no guarantee that the numbers won't slide back; they do not automatically improve each year.

Analysis by statistician Andrew Whitby of the Australian Broadcasting Corporation's popular political TV program *Q&A* between 2009 to 2013 shows that not only are more panellists male than female (2.8 vs 2 per episode), but also that women panellists speak less often than men on the show, with about two-thirds of the words spoken by men, not including the male host Tony Jones.[36] Many have also commented that women on the show are more frequently interrupted, and as it turns out, they are right. An ABC editorial review in 2015 found that 'The representation and participation of females on *Q&A* panels was significantly below that of their male counterparts … There were fewer female panelists and those that were selected were asked fewer questions and permitted far less time to speak.'[37]

What we see on the small screen reinforces and naturalises biases we already have. This is true particularly of shows that are aimed at both male and female audiences (as opposed to female-oriented daytime TV), and it happens even on shows that aim for balance, as *Q&A* expressly claims to.

Meanwhile, according to media monitoring company iSentia, women comprise only 17% of presenters at the major metropolitan talkback stations on weekdays in Australia (significantly lower than the overall percentage above). Five stations, including Sydney's 2GB, Melbourne's SEN and Perth's 6PR, are completely without female weekday presenters.[38] As writer Clementine Ford pointed out in 2014, 'Until recently only one woman in [Australia] hosted a weekday solo commercial talkback show – after March there were two.'[39] Female presenters generally have male co-hosts, or are part of the other common format of two male presenters and one female.

The male-dominated radio industry seems not to take diversity very seriously. Radio host and comedian Wendy Harmer wrote in 2012: 'It wasn't that long ago that a senior radio executive told me that men didn't want to hear two women together on talk radio … "I mean, you've been nagged all weekend by your wife and then you turn on the radio and you get nagged by TWO women," he said. And he was serious,' she added, in case there was any doubt.[40] In 2014 the top-rating FM network Triple M tweeted a picture of 25 male presenters and no women, prompting some social media criticism – yet the male dominance of radio is so common it is not often

> The perception that women's voices are too frequently heard affects the way we listen – or don't listen – to women when they speak out.

remarked upon by the general public, who presumably are used to it, and frankly lack many other listening options. Put simply, in radio, as in other media categories, a general unwillingness to listen to women (or worse, *two* women! talking! with each other!) continues to make an impact.

We can also look to analysis of Australian print media showing that despite the fact that about equal numbers of women and men are print journalists, men have twice as many front-page bylines.[41] In a typical month in the UK, 78% of front-page bylines are by men, and 84% of those quoted or mentioned are male.[42] Further, *4th Estate* website looked at six months of 2012 election coverage across all major news outlets in print, TV and radio across the US and found that an astounding 81% of all statements about the hot topic of abortion were made by men during that period. Only 12% of statements were made by women, with the remaining 7% issued by organisations.[43] One might well ask how women could have only 12% of the voice on an issue that relates directly to their own bodies' reproductive rights.

> It seems that at some level we have normalised speaking at women or speaking about women without actually speaking with them.

When we turn to our society's storytelling, we see how the issue of voice is tied up in the same male power structure. Women writers are often confined to 'women's issues', which also happen to be issues men are not expected to listen to or read about. We use terms like 'chick lit' or 'chick flick' to denote female-oriented stories. The vast majority of the directors (over 90%) and writers (over 80%) of the top-grossing films of 2011 were males, according to a 2014 report, and the vast majority of them were white.[44] In fact, 'in both 2013 and 2014, women were only 1.9% of the directors for the 100 top-grossing films'[45] – you are reading that right, *under 2%*. It took 82 years for a woman to win an Oscar for Best Director

(Kathryn Bigelow, *The Hurt Locker*, 2010). Professor Martha Lauzen of San Diego State University also reports that in 2014, 95% of cinematographers, 89% of screenwriters, 82% of editors, 81% of executive producers and 77% of producers were men.[46]

The majority of speaking roles in film are also, as it happens, for white males. The Media, Diversity, and Social Change Initiative at the University of Southern California analysed the 100 top-grossing films each year from 2007 and 2014 and found that in those 700 films, roughly 70% of speaking characters were male, and 30% were female.[47] The mainstream storytelling norm even today is a world where almost all characters are straight, the vast majority are white, and most are male.

I often joke that though I loved the classic Star Wars film *The Empire Strikes Back* as a child, I now realise the most unrealistic thing about the film is not the creatures, droids, space travel or the mystical Force, but the fact that there is one known woman in the universe – Princess Leia, who was the love interest of both male protagonists and was literally the only named female character. No wonder I wanted to be Han Solo, Luke Skywalker, even Darth Vader – anyone but the princess they fought over, who in *Return of the Jedi* ends up chained to Jabba the Hutt in a gold bikini. When emulating adventurous behaviour I was called 'tomboy', further cementing the idea that being adventurous was the domain of those born with a penis. I may not have consciously noticed a gender disparity – after all, I was under 10 – but I noticed that the men had all the fun, and that just seemed to be the way things were. (Thankfully, kids watching Star Wars in 2016 have a more diverse world to take in, with notably more women and more racial diversity in *The Force Awakens*.[48])

> The mainstream storytelling norm even today is a world where almost all characters are straight, the vast majority are white, and most are male.

It seems that at some level we have normalised speaking *at* women or speaking *about* women without actually speaking *with* them. This is just as true for other marginalised groups. The heterosexual perspective is normalised (heteronormativity), and in Western culture, the white viewpoint is also unconsciously regarded as the norm. Individuals in any of the groups outside of these norms may speak often amongst themselves, but are less often heard by others. In other words, *talking amongst yourselves* is different from *speaking out*.

Speaking out matters

...

None of this should suggest that *all* men speak more frequently than *all* women in *all* situations, or that all men are viewed more favourably than all women. This is large-scale data, remember. Context matters, individual interactions and personalities differ, and as with other patterns of human interaction, factors in addition to gender play a role, including race, class, disability, sexual orientation, age and so on. As a consistent pattern, however, we are less used to hearing women speak out than men, and more likely to interrupt or criticise women when they do.

Many men and boys could also be taught to listen more and speak less. There is a complex set of social pressures encouraging them to believe they need to assert their authority by always speaking out, even when they may not be the expert in the room.

'Calm down' and the particularly telling 'Shhhh' are still fallbacks for men (and even some women) who don't like being challenged by women. Many who do it would deny that this is an implicitly sexist manoeuvre, yet adult men, though sometimes interrupted by others, are rarely given the 'Shhhh'. 'Shhhh' is reserved for perceived underlings, usually women and children, who are supposed to be seen and not heard.

It matters that women keep speaking despite these interruptions and patronising attempts at silencing. As author Rebecca Solnit writes in *Men Explain Things to Me* (2014), silencing is a major obstacle in '[t]he battle for women to be treated like human beings with rights to life, liberty, and the pursuit of involvement in cultural and political arenas'.[49]

It matters.

CHAPTER 2

UNCONSCIOUS BIAS

Unconscious bias

...

Many of us, regardless of gender, would like to believe we are free of personal biases. But the cumulative effect of hearing men more than women over a long period of time has been that male voices, perspectives and issues are more often promoted, and the male voice overall is 'normalised' as the standard speaking position.

This bias towards the male voice or perspective is rarely intentionally sexist – though of course there are exceptions, like literature professor and author David Gilmour, who famously said, 'I'm not interested in teaching books by women … What I teach is guys. Serious heterosexual guys.'[1] (He's excluding women – and non-heterosexual men – and he knows it.) But whether the rest of us are consciously aware of it or not, we are likely to view authority, achievement, merit and communication style differently depending on whether we believe it is coming from a man or a woman.

This is generally referred to as **unconscious bias**. It means that showing leadership, or taking the stage to speak out, can earn women (and other groups affected by unconscious bias) a variety of responses that may not always be strictly tied to the merit of their arguments. And left unaddressed, it can subtly or not-so-subtly colour our view of the world, ourselves and others.

> We are likely to view authority, achievement, merit and communication style differently depending on whether we believe it is coming from a man or a woman.

Stats and facts

...

Let's look briefly at a few relevant stats. As we know, roughly half of the human population is born female and roughly half is born male, with the remainder being people who are defined as intersex, or who do not identify with either gender. In fact, in many continents, including Australia and North America, there are slightly *more* females than males in the population.

Despite all this, it took 109 years before there was a female Australian prime minister, no woman has ever been US president, and only four women in the US have become Supreme Court justices. As of January 2015, only 17% of government ministers worldwide were women, with the majority overseeing sectors like education and family.[2] That means 83% of ministers are male, legislating for all of the population. We must acknowledge that having more than four men's voices for every one woman's voice is a disproportionately *male* version of 'democracy'.

Outside the political arena, in the UK's National Gallery, out of 2300 works, there are only 10 paintings by women,[3] and The Royal Institute of British Architects has awarded its most prestigious honour, the Royal Gold Medal, to an individual woman only once in 168-year history of the award (in 2016 to Zaha Hadid). In sport, only 8% of Australia's sponsorship dollars flow to female players and only 7% of media coverage is of women's sport.[4] As ABC sports journalist Amanda Shalala points out:

> While women's sport continues to grow on the pitch, with the likes of the Matildas [soccer], Diamonds [netball], and Southern Stars [cricket] producing exceptional performances on the world stage, sportswomen are still mistreated in almost all off field areas. The pay gap is enormous, with many female athletes

paid below the minimum wage, the amount of media coverage they receive has remained at the same embarrassingly low level for decades, sponsorship figures are paltry, and there are still nowhere near enough women in senior leadership positions.[5]

Now, all these disparate statistics could represent anomalies. Or, as some defenders of the status quo are quick to point out, it could be that with few exceptions, only men want to go into politics or design public spaces. It may be that women don't like to paint or play sport.

Could be.

Or it could be that these various stats all confirm something any historian should be able to tell you: that there is a history of excluding women from positions of power and influence, and a history of overlooking women's achievements in favour of men's.

There was a time when that was a stated goal, in fact, a point of principle. In 1873 Harvard president Edward Clarke famously argued against women's education, claiming that the blood demanded by the brain would prevent the female reproductive system from developing properly. Women weren't supposed to be 'capable' of getting an education or participating in the democratic process. They weren't *supposed* to be able to vote or stand for office.

There are still clear reminders of this history in our schools, universities, public institutions and even public parks. As of 2015 there are 22 statues of historical figures in New York's famous Central Park, and all are of men.[6] And out of 573 listed statues commemorating important people around the UK, 15% are of women, with most of those being characters from Greek and Roman mythology, as there are apparently so few real women who have done things.

Yes, we are getting much better at permitting women to participate in public life – we've made it legal, for starters – but that isn't to say we are all particularly comfortable with it.

Gender isn't everything, but it isn't nothing either.

So how do we actually know unconscious bias exists? This is where studies are helpful. For example, in one study of a group of students who did not see their instructors in person,[7] researchers 'found that the instructor whom students thought was male received higher ratings on all 12 traits, regardless of whether the instructor was actually male or female', the lead researcher, Lillian MacNell, explained.[8] These sorts of ratings naturally have an impact on promotion and tenure opportunities for women in academia.

Likewise, a paper published in the US examined the results of a randomised double-blind study. Half of a group of scientists were given a job application with a male name attached, and half were given the exact same application with a female name attached. Remember, both applications are the same. They show the same CV, the same accomplishments and abilities. The results 'found that the "female" applicants were rated significantly lower than the "males" in competence, hireability, and whether the scientist would be willing to mentor the student'. The scientists also offered lower starting salaries to the female-named applicants. Apparently the scientists who judged the applications were both male and female, showing – the authors of the study claimed – that a bias against women exists in both genders.[9] There are many such studies,[10] and even studies suggesting gender bias against gender bias studies. That's right, 'men evaluate the quality of research unveiling this bias as less meritorious than do women.'[11] Again, if you aren't experiencing it, you are less likely to believe it happens. Likewise, if the conclusions of a study challenge your status in any way, you are keener to dismiss it.

We have already looked at how we more frequently hear from men and more frequently interrupt women. Add to that the way we perceive women differently – rating their performances more harshly, or judging them less 'hireable' or 'professional' and worthy of a lower salary – and you can see how powerfully unconscious bias is at work. Another symptom of that is the way we understand **merit**.

A word on merit

...

Not all of us will find ourselves speaking out about the underrepresentation of women in particular areas of power and influence – politics, the arts, sport and so on. Those who do, however, will likely hear about something called merit.

In the West, we're told we live in a meritocracy. And in a meritocracy, this thing called merit always wins out. I'm often told, 'Just do the work and you will be rewarded.' It will happen naturally, and you won't need to overcome any existing biases to get a promotion or award. Merit can be seen and rewarded in anyone, regardless of race, gender, sexual orientation or disability.

Hard work and merit are the great equalisers, you see. But the problem, according to our unconscious bias, is that not enough women have the ability, or are prepared to put in the work. Besides, women don't want power and they don't do the things they should to get ahead. Forget that according to the Australian Bureau of Statistics, more women than men aged 20 to 39 now have university qualifications;[12] the fact remains that women naturally lack ambition and ability – right?

Despite all this insistence that we live in a flawless meritocracy, some people just don't get it. For example, when Professor Eric Schliesser was invited to yet another philosophy conference with no female speakers, he decided he'd had enough. He teamed up with another male philosopher to issue a clarion call to male philosophers who 'through their inaction, complacency, and indifference contribute to the sexist status quo'.[13]

> The cumulative effect of hearing men more than women over a long period of time has been that male voices, perspectives and issues are more often promoted, and the male voice over all is 'normalised' as the standard speaking position.

They decided to boycott events where females were excluded. 'We hereby commit ourselves not to accept invitations to male-only events,' the pair wrote. Their boycott divided the philosophy community, and accusations of tokenism soon followed. Yet Professor Schliesser rejected those accusations as 'bogus'. 'The tokenism argument is just insane for two reasons,' Schliesser told the *National Post*. 'A lot of the men that show up are in their own way tokens – they're [an organiser's] friend, they're your supervisor, there are people that are over the hill, that show up drunk … And number two, there are, in fact, lots of very good female philosophers.'[14]

He is wrong, of course. Connections couldn't have anything to do with it. The first conference in Berlin that he boycotted had 14 male speakers because there were no women who had enough merit to be included, that's all. That Professor Eric Schliesser has 'personally organized 45 successful gender-balanced conferences in five years' only shows his pitiful lack of understanding of 'merit'. Right?

Yes, we can laugh, but this belief in a flawlessly functioning meritocracy is still the most frequently cited excuse for all kinds of inequalities, abuses and human rights atrocities. It's also the excuse for why women are repeatedly excluded from positions of leadership – and for why other groups who have not traditionally held the reins of power happen to still find themselves marginalised.

The myth of 'meritocracy' was the reason used for former Prime Minister Tony Abbott's selection of a 100% white and 90% male first cabinet. Merit does seem curiously specific in certain circles of power, doesn't it? At the time of writing, diversity in cabinet had improved somewhat, with a gender breakdown of five women (23.8%) and 16 men (76.1%) in PM Malcolm Turnbull's first cabinet.[15] The total ministry at the moment includes nine women (21.4%) and 33 men (78.5%), slightly ahead of the world average – with the majority being white males (78.5%) with Anglo-Celtic ancestry (over 78%), and under 5% having Aboriginal ancestry.

That overbalance towards one demographic – white males of Anglo-Celtic heritage – has been in place for so long that a white ministry that is over 78% male can still be heralded as a 'win for diversity' as it governs over all of the considerably more diverse nation. As writer and Aboriginal activist Celeste Liddle has tweeted: 'Note to media: 5 female Ministers is not a "win for women". That's actually less than a third of the cabinet. Your bar is too low.'[16]

'I believe in people being promoted on merit,' Julie Bishop said in 2013 of being the sole female in Tony Abbott's cabinet, consisting of one woman and 19 men. 'I have now been appointed by Tony Abbott as Australia's first female foreign minister. This is one of the most senior positions of government. I don't see a glass ceiling.'[17] She is entitled to her opinion, of course, but her words seemed to suggest that she believed there had never before been any Australian women with enough merit to hold the position of foreign minister, or any other women in her party with sufficient merit to make it into the cabinet. Is it likely that there are so few women in cabinet solely because of lack of merit among the 50% of the adult population who identify as women? Hmm. Or could 2013 Australian of the Year Ita Buttrose be right when she claims that 'The glass ceiling still does exist in Australia. We're told it doesn't, but that's just nonsense'?[18]

Meanwhile, in Canada in 2015 the newly elected Trudeau government achieved 50/50 gender representation with its multicultural and diverse cabinet. Many also pointed out that numerous female ministers held impressive professional credentials relating to their portfolios, with the minister of health being a doctor; the minister of science having worked with a team that won a Nobel Prize in 2007; and the minister of sport and persons with disabilities being a legally blind former Paralympian athlete with a law degree.[19] Those are just three out of the fifteen women included in the thirty-one person cabinet. All of them have impressive credentials. And the point is: the population can be more fairly and democratically represented in corridors of power; it's just that it rarely is.

There is a history of excluding women from positions of power and influence, and a history of overlooking women's achievements in favour of men's.

Around the world, positions of political leadership are disproportionately taken up by men, yet their decisions have an impact on all of us. This affects individual lives and decisions, but it also affects us in a multitude of ways. A more equitable distribution of influence, power and wealth would go some way toward alleviating many of the problems in our world today.

According to independent watchdog Freedom House, 'Of 24 peace negotiations from 2000 to 2011, more than half featured women's participation of 5% or less. In nine of these 24 – Somalia (twice), Côte d'Ivoire, Nepal, Central African Republic (twice), Zimbabwe, Iraq, and Yemen – women were completely excluded.'[20] The fact is, we can't afford to continue to shut out the half of the population who are born female.

And the issue isn't just the invisibility of women and other groups, it is the invisibility of the invisibility, and the hostile reception waiting for those who mention it.

Is merit important? Yes. Undoubtedly. You can't do the job without the skills. Is 'merit' everything that's going on here? I say no way. Talent, ability, hard work and merit are incredibly important factors, but also work within a larger power structure that allows more opportunity to some than others, and a system of influence, expectation and privilege that places certain stories, certain voices, certain types of work and certain abilities above others. Those voices, abilities and types of work just happen to be disproportionately the domain of those who are in power under the current system.

We 'see' merit differently in different people. Most of you, this book's readers, will benefit from some aspects of the current system, while being disadvantaged in other ways. For example, I benefited as a white woman born of a lower middle class family. I got a decent public education in Canada and now, through my professional career, I have managed to enrol in university as a mature-age part-time student because I have saved enough money to do so. That is a classic combination of privilege and work, but while I acknowledge the work, some of it hard work, I can't deny the privilege. I could have been born to a very poor family, rather than lower middle class. I could have been born with a different ancestry that set me apart from the main demographic holding the power. I could have been born in a country with more gender inequality than Canada, or a country where I could not gain access to a good education through the public system. The list goes on.

So where does all this leave merit? We can reward and acknowledge hard work, enterprise, ability and 'merit' while also recognising that some people have a tougher journey to get access to those same opportunities than others. Put simply, the playing field is not level, as much as we'd like to think it is; not for women and not for other marginalised groups (with racism, ableism, homophobia, transphobia, ageism and classism also playing major roles). The gendered dynamics of power, influence and what we hear as the public 'voice' mean that the 50% of the population identifying as 'female', more often than not, has to work harder to gain that reward for merit, or to have their merit recognised.

Marginalised voices matter. Women's voices matter. We would all benefit from more women and other marginalised people speaking out – and more people listening without bias when they do.

Yes, we are getting much better at permitting women to participate in public life – we've made it legal, for starters – but that isn't to say we are all particularly comfortable with it. Gender isn't everything, but it isn't nothing either.

Now, *that* is a reality check with merit.

Be aware of unconscious bias

So what do you do, knowing about the potential for unconscious bias when you speak out as a woman? There are a few things:

1. Listen with less bias. Be aware of unconscious bias when you are listening to or judging the performance of everyone (including men, women, those who are differently gendered, or LGBTIQ, those who are from a different racial group etc) and try to minimise your bias.

2. Prepare yourself thoroughly. Then speak out, aware that you know your stuff. (See PART TWO: HOW TO SPEAK OUT.) When you know your stuff you are much more likely to be confident of your position.

3. Speak out. Do this in your own way, regardless of the potential backlash. (See PART THREE: WHAT TO EXPECT WHEN YOU SPEAK OUT.) There is power in numbers. The more women who speak out, the more normalised it will become. It won't happen overnight, as our unconscious biases have had centuries to form, but we can undo them with time.

4. Look after yourself. Know that sometimes you will encounter backlash. With that in mind, you need to look after yourself particularly well. (See PART THREE, particularly **Chapter 15: Self-Care**.)

PART 2

HOW TO SPEAK OUT

If you do not speak for yourself, others will likely speak for you. This has a particular history for women, who in their public and private lives often had others advocate for or against them, without allowing them to be part of the conversation at all, either by law or social convention. Now that women can get into those rooms and spaces, can be part of those conversations, those who are able to should. Take up that space. Speak out. Participate. And do it in your own way.

There are different ways to 'speak out', and not all of them make a sound. Some people express themselves, or 'speak out' in ways that do not use any forms of formal speech – through art, photography, film, music or through their bodies in the form of dance or other expressions. Others, like myself, often speak out through their writing, in the form of books, blogs, online posts or articles, opinion pieces and journalism (see **Chapter 5** on writing). Still others use formal language that is not spoken. In Australia, for example, about one in six people have hearing loss, and tens of thousands use Auslan (Australian sign language). Protests are a powerful form of speech, and likewise craftivism [activism centered on practices of craft] or other forms of political expression.

Your speaking out may be a part of your professional work, or as part of not-for-profit fundraising and advocacy. It may be a primary focus of your time and energy, or it may take a smaller role. I recommend you focus on the mediums and methods that most inspire you. I also recommend that you begin by using your existing experience and knowledge, and then stay open to what other forms you might engage in.

CHAPTER 3

THE VOICE

Women's voices – from valley speak to vocal fry

...

Speaking out can convey messages and ideas to an audience of one, or an audience of millions. Even for those who prefer to do their speaking out using a typewriter, keyboard, visual image or protest sign, there will be times when they will be called upon to put their case to an audience verbally, whether it be at a one-on-one meeting, or in a boardroom, a radio or TV studio, or a lecture hall or stage in front of thousands.

Naturally, the speaker's voice will not only be the *vehicle* for the speaker's messages but can also convey its own messages – including some things we may not have intended to convey, like distress, or a lack of authority or credibility. With listening being as subjective as it is, we can never fully control the way we come across to listeners (more on this shortly). However, we can control our message and some of its impact, and we can also put in work to make ourselves more comfortable speaking in front of a few people or even large groups, in what might be considered nerve-racking situations. The more comfortable we are, the more likely we are to accept subsequent opportunities to speak out, and the better we are able to perform and hone our skills through repetition and experience.

Displaying clear signs of intense nervousness tends to undermine a speaker's message. But even when you clearly enunciate and avoid any signs of debilitating nerves, the content of your words may suffer due to perceptions of your voice, tone or speech patterns. Men's voices, rather than the content of their speech, tend to be critically scrutinised in this way only when deemed unusual due to speech impediments, strong accents that make speech difficult to understand, and speech patterns that interrupt traditional concepts of masculinity, sexuality and gender roles. If a man has a high-pitched voice or lisp, this is thought by some to be damaging to him, as it is perceived as feminine. A stutter is thought to convey weakness and hesitation, also traits thought by some to be feminine. For women, speech impediments, stutters and strong accents can also garner criticism, but from there things get even more complicated.

Women speaking in the public eye, without obvious nervousness, stutters or speech impediments, frequently find their voice quality or tone remarked upon, sometimes to the exclusion of any comment on or engagement with their actual words and arguments. There are the accusations of sounding 'shrill' or 'hysterical' (like Senator Penny Wong in **Chapter 1**), and there are also complaints about sounding 'grating', 'ditzy' or 'like an airhead' – and some even more inventive insults like this one sent to the Nine Network about accomplished reporters Lisa Wilkinson and Georgie Gardner: 'Hello Producer. I am totally fed up with the combination of Lisa and Georgie they're shocking together and it's like listening to a chorus of cats.'[1]

It's worth remembering that advising women about their voices is nothing new – just like advising women to be silent. *Woman's World*, a comprehensive late-1950s manual for women on beauty, cooking, etiquette and deportment, has a chapter called 'Voicing Your Charm'.[2] Some of the advice is helpful, and includes avoiding the excessive use of 'like' or 'um' in sentences, and making sure *what* you have to say is worthwhile.

Fortunately, not many people these days will openly admit to not wanting to listen to women, but a surprisingly large number of people still angrily comment on how annoying women's voices are, apparently in the belief that the female-ness of the speaker is not the issue, but that they just 'sound wrong'. When not being criticised for sounding shrill, women tend to cop complaints for things like valleyspeak (a style of speaking originating in Southern California's

San Fernando Valley, which became internationally popular for a time, featuring rising intonation and frequent use of words like 'totally' and 'like') and uptalk (ending sentences with an upward inflection), or having nasal, high-pitched or breathy voices.

They're also censured for something called 'vocal fry' or 'creaky voice': speaking in the lower register of their voices until it creates a 'fry' – glottalisation, or that creaky guttural popping sound in the back of the throat. It became headline news in 2015 because there was an apparent 'epidemic' of young women who spoke this way. (Numerous news reports actually used that very term, epidemic, as if women's use of vocal fry were on par with polio.)

It is less often pointed out that many men also speak this way, including actors Al Pacino[3] and Bruce Willis,[4] and noted linguist, philosopher and political commentator Noam Chomsky.[5] Linguistics professor Mark Liberman contends that the 'low creaky vibrations' of vocal fry 'have been common since forever'[6] among both men and women, though previously they were more notable amongst – yep – men, because their voices tend to be lower in the register to begin with. Casey Klofstad, Associate Professor of Political Science at the University of Miami, observed in a radio interview that 'Lower-pitched voices are seen as more authoritative, more dominant and, in men, more sexually attractive. So one could make a reasonable argument that if a woman sort of lowers her voice to the lowest register, as one does with vocal fry, that maybe that's a way for her to connote those positive characteristics.' Then he added: 'But, on the other hand, there are folks like you and me personally who find the affectation off-putting.'[7]

Radio and TV presenter Howard Stern, author of *Private Parts* and the man who brought us *The Miss Howard Stern New Year's Eve Pageant*, featuring 'Miss Fried Egg Tits' and 'Miss Good Head', called vocal fry 'the most annoying thing ever'[8] – evidently without a trace of irony. On the popular radio program *This American*

Life, host Ira Glass explained that they had recently 'been getting a lot of hate mail about the young women on our staff – listeners complain about their "vocal fry"... These are some of the angriest emails we ever

> Naturally, the speaker's voice will not only be the vehicle for the speaker's messages but can also convey its own messages – including some things we may not have intended to convey.

get. They call these women's voices "unbearable", "excruciating", "annoyingly adolescent", "beyond annoying", "difficult to pay attention", "so severe as to cause discomfort", "can't stand the pain", "distractingly disgusting", "could not get over how annoyed I was", "I am so appalled", "detracts from the credibility of the journalist", "degrades the value of the reportage", "it's a choice", "very unprofessional",' he said.

It is apparently a speech crime of dire consequence, often described as being Kardashian-like.[9] But such objections seem to have more to do with the words being said (Kardashian speak vs Chomsky speak) or who is saying them (female vs male) than with the actual 'fry'. Mark Liberman points out that the most common user of vocal fry on *This American Life* would actually be Ira Glass himself, yet it is the female staff who are the focus of hate mail.[10] It is telling that Howard Stern lamented about women who switch between their 'feminine voices' and 'annoying' vocal fry, implying that vocal fry is specifically unfeminine.[11] Gravelly voices in men have traditionally been deemed authoritative, even sexy. In women, they're unfeminine, annoying, offputting, an epidemic.

The 2014 study[12] most often cited in the 'epidemic' articles is one that concludes we judge women more harshly than men for the same verbal tics – ranking them as less hireable and less 'trustworthy'. But while studies like this are interesting, the recent widespread public concern about young women and their vocal cords does seem to be prompted mostly by media reports, rather than scholars.

And the gendered nature of the criticism doesn't just relate to verbal fry. For example, valley speak tends to be regional (Southern California's San Fernando Valley) and age-specific (young adult) more than gender-specific, but again we see that the public concern is very much focused on women. Or consider the word 'like'. When you think of someone who uses that word a lot as a filler in conversation, what kind of person comes to mind? Would that person be, say, female? Perhaps even blonde? Mark Liberman analysed 12,000 phone conversations and discovered that although young people used filler words such as 'like' more often than people of older generations, men actually used the terms 'in, like, the' and 'on, like, the' *more* often than women, and concluded: 'there's no evidence that women insert non-traditional like into their conversation more often than men do.'[13]

(On the topic of how women's presentation style is judged, ever heard of 'Resting Bitch Face' or 'RBF'? That thing where some women, when they don't smile, look, well, 'bitchy'? Some researchers went ahead and studied it,[14] and they 'detected RBF in male and female faces in equal measure',[15] explains one of the authors of the study, Abbe Macbeth. 'Which means that the idea of RBF as a predominantly female phenomenon has little to do with facial physiology and more to do with social norms.'' Again, it appears we often judge women more harshly for traits common in both sexes.)

Some of the criticism or 'guidance' directed at women's speech is well intended, of course – if women's voice habits *do* affect their employability, we all want them to have their best chance in the job market etc. But the fact that so many people have issues with women's voices suggests a much larger and more objectionable issue of unconscious bias (see **Chapter 2**). This issue – which might be summed up as 'We judge women more harshly than men for the same things' – doesn't seem as popular as the usual headlines about what women are doing wrong.

This suggests to me that when I don't like a woman's voice I should probably take pause and consider why. What is it that sounds wrong? And why am I noticing her voice and not what she has to say? In a *Guardian* article under the headline 'Young women, give up the vocal fry and reclaim your strong female voice', Naomi Wolf wrote that 'The problem of young women's voices is gaining new cultural visibility … What is heartbreaking about the current trend for undermining female voice is that this is the most transformational generation of young women ever.'[16]

I don't tend to 'fry', but I will say this all sounds a little too familiar. Early in my career, after any of my TV appearances, or after narrating one of several audio books of my work, I often found myself criticised by members of the public for my 'weird' voice because of my Canadian–Australian accent, or told I sound 'like a man', presumably because my voice is not high-pitched enough. Confusingly, I would often – and sometimes on the very same day – be praised in equal measure for having a 'sexy' voice or 'a voice I could listen to all day'.

Weird, masculine, or sexy?

It all sounds quite dire.

This tendency to have people focus on my voice has lessened somewhat as I've become older and also better known – perhaps because more people now recognise that this is just how I sound, and maybe also because I now have more of 'a voice', in the sense of a higher profile. Perhaps my public speaking voice has also improved – it would be natural for this to happen with experience – but if I did somehow become a better speaker it is not easy to pick what I changed.

In all of this commentary about my voice there was a distinct sense that for some, a woman's voice, particularly a young woman's voice, was distracting – a bit like her appearance – and that something needed to be said about it. Some portion of the population found it difficult to focus on the content of my words, and instead were considerably more interested in commenting on, complimenting or policing my appearance, body shape, clothing choices, hairstyle, make-up, accent and voice tone. It's hard to say just what changed, but as I got older people became less concerned – though not completely unconcerned – with my voice and more concerned with the content of my words.

Thanks to advertising, women are visually prominent in much of the media, but in this context are often seen and not heard. And only certain kinds of women are highly visible – young, thin, white, middle or upper class, cisgender, straight.

We see a lot of women. They seem to be everywhere. But we don't listen to them. They are one-dimensional. Perhaps this is one reason why women's voices are so often remarked upon, closely scrutinised, and complimented or demonised when they are heard. If your voice is too high it is shrill. If it is too low or has too much 'fry' it's annoying or masculine. If you speak too much you are bossy. If you don't speak enough you only have yourself to blame for your lack of success or participation. Sexy or unsexy, too high or too low, there is always someone with something to say about the way a woman speaks.

What if women 'fix' their speech? What if they successfully avoid saying 'like', or avoid talking in the wrong pitch, or with vocal fry? (While you can edit out your own quirks and tics in your writing, all this can be hard to achieve in speech, of course.)

What if women could just talk more like men? As linguist Dr Deborah Tannen points out, 'But if they [women] talk in ways that are associated with authority, and are seen as too aggressive, then that, too, is their fault when people react negatively.'[17]

With all this to contend with, it would be understandable for some women to wonder just what they should be focusing on. Avoiding verbal tics? Or just trying to be less female?

One thing cuts through all of this, and it is the focus I keep in mind every time I speak out.

Focus on your content and suggest others do the same.

While we can all probably do things to improve our professional voices – we'll look more closely at how to adapt the voice below and in the next chapter – it is also vitally important to know that some criticism really isn't about you, or your voice, at all. Some people still have a problem with women's voices, and that is *their* problem, not the problem of the women they are criticising. Whatever you do, don't let criticism of your voice silence you.

· ·

Using your voice with confidence

When using your voice to speak out try to breathe and speak from the diaphragm (down in the belly) rather than the chest or throat. (See **Using your diaphragm** on page 73.) Speak calmly and slowly, at the lower end of your natural voice register. This will tend to make both you and your audience feel more at ease. Practise this at home and before your speeches or presentations until this style of speaking is second nature to you. (Of course, speaking 'slowly' is relative and you will want to adjust your speed to suit your personal style and your audience so it feels natural to you. But keep in mind that very fast speech often connotes nervousness or lack of authority, and is generally something to be avoided.)

· ·

No two people speak precisely the same way, but if there are orators you admire, watch videos of them speaking and take note of their style, the way they use their voice and their tone. What is it that you like about their message and style of speaking? Do they tend to use a deep voice or high voice? Do they speak slowly or quickly? Do they use pauses? How do they use their hands when they speak? Make a brief study of speakers you admire and think about how their techniques might be applied to your own speaking. The idea is not to copy, but to become aware of what your preferences are, what is effective, and what you can do to become more confident and powerful when you speak out.

Most importantly, prepare your content thoroughly beforehand, so you know what you have to say. (See the next chapter.) Once you begin, stay focused on the content of your speech, rather than others' perceptions of you or your voice.

If you are criticised for your voice:
- Ask them 'Why?' Often critics, when addressed, won't really have an answer to why your voice seems objectionable to them.
- Suggest your critic would be better off trying to concentrate on the *content* of your words, rather than their personal perception of your tone.

A personal anecdote

...

Last year I spoke at a literary event in an Australian town. When I arrived in that town, I became aware that the conservative prime minister of the time, Tony Abbott, had recently visited and was particularly popular with the prominent mining community there, many of whom were to be present at the event where I was giving my keynote speech. After one look at the heavily male, conservative and mining-oriented crowd at this literary event I realised that some of those present would not be on side, as it were, as I delivered my planned speech on gender equality and women's rights. After many years of experience I can sometimes tell how much pushback I am likely to get, just by walking into a room. With just a few minutes to make any last minute decisions about my pre-planned speech, I had to decide what to do. I was not there simply to entertain, though I hoped to do that also. I would not alter my speech, which was well researched and worth being heard, simply because I suspected some of the audience would find it uncomfortable. I went up and spoke as planned, on the topic that was in line with the client's brief, to that audience of several hundred guests, and it started out just fine.

When I walked on stage and introduced myself the room was full of smiles and applause. By about 10 minutes into my speech the tuxedoed arms started folding. By 20 minutes in there was palpable discomfort in the room – frowns, noticeable tension. By 30 minutes in the topiaries were wilting and the balloons had slowly drifted to the floor. Of course my planned piece happened to have a Tony Abbott bit in it, he was PM after all, and when I mentioned that he had once said, 'I think it would be folly to expect that women will ever dominate or even approach equal representation in a large number of areas simply because their aptitudes, abilities and interests are different for physiological reasons',[18] and that I hoped he had since changed his mind as he was currently Minister for Women, well, there was what could be described as deafening silence in the hall. It was a planned part of my speech, relevant to the topic the client wanted me to speak on, and I continued smiling and speaking confidently throughout, the result of years of practice. When I finished there was barely any sound in the huge hall, perhaps a smattering of applause from a few tables. I walked off the stage, sat back at my table and no one spoke to me. I smiled and sipped my water. The entire experience was highly unusual, but I'd picked that it was a possibility immediately on seeing the crowd. After about half an hour the women in the room started coming up, however. One by one they took me aside and whispered about how certain 'old blokes just don't get it' etc. They bought copies of my book and wanted it signed, and said they would give it to their daughters, their friends. By the end of the night I had been approached by perhaps every woman in that hall, all 200 of them, along with the other authors there, one of whom described it as one of the most 'extraordinary things' he had ever seen. 'The hostility in the room was palpable and you just kept going. Nothing was going to stop you. It was a great speech.'

Great speech or not, it was well researched and well delivered, and that is all you can do. That doesn't always mean it will be well received by every person in every crowd. (Though I did win over new fans that night, it's just that it took them a while to get up the courage to be seen with me.) This rather unusual experience of public speaking – I've experienced many rooms, male-dominated and female-dominated, but nothing quite like that – again reinforced my belief that preparation is everything. If you are confident in your message, and you have done your homework, focus on that. Say what you have to say. You deserve to be heard, and the fact that some don't like your message does not mean it isn't worth hearing.

Rediscovering your voice

...

Speaking in front of groups is, for many people, something that must be learned and fought for. The natural voice often needs to be consciously rediscovered. If you are going to be speaking in public often, work on what speech improvements you can, while knowing that not all criticism of your voice will really be about you, as discussed in the previous chapter.

Get professional guidance if you feel it will be a good investment. If you are planning a career or lifestyle that involves a lot of public speaking, it is, in my view, worth considering a few sessions with a good voice coach. I did this for a short time in the late 1990s (only two sessions, admittedly) to help overcome my nervousness about public speaking, which would trigger me to breathe from my upper chest rather than my diaphragm. (See **Using your diaphragm** on page 73.)

Once I learned to breathe properly, and avoid the shallow breathing I was getting trapped into while speaking publicly (largely the result of nerves), it became much easier for me to address crowds. My tone, pace and ability to concentrate on what I was saying fell into line much more readily. Now I get into a natural public speaking rhythm when I take the stage.

Whether or not you decide that voice coaching and professional training in public speaking are worthwhile investments for you, it can be helpful to observe your body and voice when speaking in front of large groups and remind yourself to breathe deeply and slow down. You can view voice training or research of this kind as a professional aspect of your

> Speaking in front of groups is, for many people, something that must be learned and fought for. The natural voice often needs to be consciously rediscovered.

chosen vocation, like learning code is for a programmer. It is just a thing you need to learn for a time so you can do your job well, and you *will* be able to do it well if you set your mind to it.

Making it seem natural

For many women, speaking out can feel 'unnatural'. I know, because I've experienced it. And in truth there *is* something unnatural, or at least highly unusual, about being in a room with dozens, hundreds or even thousands of people, knowing they are all there to listen to one person: you.

'Why me?', I will sometimes think – not out of self-pity, but as a legitimate question. 'Why should all of these people with their various skills, accomplishments and life experiences listen to me right now?'

Well, I have to give them a reason, don't I? I have to have a reason for getting up there, and that reason must be that I have something to say. I must speak with intent. My way of speaking with intent is to do my research well and to know my stuff as thoroughly as possible (see **Chapter 5: Knowing Your Stuff**). Those things take a lot of the nerves away, and give me confidence that what I have to say is worth hearing.

After my first book was published, I went from rarely speaking publicly to being required to do a lot of it. I had spent much of my time writing books or reading them. Thanks to the modelling career that had paid my bills so I could write, I had lived a significant part of my life being seen and not heard. I had not really found my voice in the sense that I have now, nor had I used my voice fully. The expectation, as someone who was becoming a public figure for her writing, was that I would automatically be able to speak in public, as if it were a natural thing. It was just speaking, after all. Speaking is something we all do to communicate and survive, but doing it publicly was not easy and did not feel natural to me.

I never quite succumbed to vomiting before a speech, but in the early days I came close. I had a maddening tendency to be overwhelmed by internal panic. For the launch of my first book, *Fetish*, in 1999, I wisely wrote a speech. Unfortunately, however, inside a fairly calm-looking exterior (or so those who were there insist) my heart was pounding so hard it was all I could hear. At the podium at the packed Justice & Police Museum in Sydney, I looked up from my notes to speak and then couldn't find my place on the page again, and all those chosen words went out the window. I thanked my publisher three times and forgot to thank my agent (who has since forgiven me, though we still laugh about it). In short, I could not quite function.

By practising public speaking skills I have not only learned to function when giving a speech, but have actually learned to enjoy it.

In this chapter and the next, I will explain how that transformation took place, and the steps you can take to help that change happen for you.

Relearning childhood lessons

One of the keys to being able to speak out publicly, while remaining your thinking, functioning self, is to believe you have the right to be there and the right to be heard. As we saw earlier in the chapter, this can sometimes be a particular challenge for women and girls who may have been discouraged from speaking up, or even taught that they will be punished for doing so. In my case, in my teens I was often discouraged from thinking I had something to say. This is unfortunately common. For many of us, rediscovering our voice is a vital first step.

I asked voice coach Lucy Cornell,[19] author of *Connect and Inspire*,[20] why this is, and what tips she has for rediscovering your voice. She explains:

The skills required to express yourself are natural to everyone. The problem is that most adults, men and women, have lost access to their natural, vocal expressivity. When you are a baby you have a full vocal range connected to your emotional and intellectual needs. At this age, we are extremely persuasive and expressive. One of the key functions of the voice is to help us to survive. When we were babies, we felt hungry – we cried, we had a tummy pain – we cried, we saw Mummy and Daddy's face – we cooed and made sounds that drew them closer ... At around three years, we learn to civilise the voice: 'pull it together', 'be quiet', 'tone it down'. We learn to civilise the voice in order to survive within our society. This is also where gender distinctions begin guiding us as to what voice is appropriate to survive as a boy or girl. These distinctions are not arbitrary. They are deeply connected to the culture we exist in. Depending on culture, girls may be taught to 'Speak softly', 'Be a good little girl with a quiet voice', 'Speak sweetly', 'Don't be so noisy', 'Little girls should be seen and not heard' etc.

And as we know, this is precisely what still happens: disproportionately, women are still seen and not heard (see **Chapter 1: Shhh**). Women are much more rarely the central characters, the experts, the leaders. As film director Shira Piven told the *New York Times*: 'I feel that there is something going on underneath all of this which is the idea that women aren't quite as interesting as men. That men have heroic lives, do heroic things, are these kind of warriors in the world, and that women have a certain set of rooms that they have to operate in.'[21]

Many women internalise this. They feel, on some level, that extending themselves beyond that 'set of rooms' is not only a risk (it is a risk for everyone), but also unfeminine, brash, vulgar, even unacceptable.

Whether or not we remember it, for many of us, those ideas have been reinforced from birth, even by the best-intentioned people. In fact, well-meaning teachers, parents or guardians will often try to bring a child up to fit the prevailing gender stereotypes and expectations precisely because they don't want you to stand out in a way that might be socially awkward for you. They want you to fit in.

> One of the keys to being able to speak out publicly, while remaining your thinking, functioning self, is to believe you have the right to be there and the right to be heard.

Boys may be discouraged from crying or showing sensitivity or pain. Girls may be discouraged from speaking too loudly, or being sporty or adventurous. In this way, certain parts of ourselves may be suppressed through regular reinforcement over time.

These gender expectations are rarely challenged directly. They remain a kind of background noise or a normative baseline. We try to conform, and when we don't, most of us will come up against some kind of pushback for not sticking to those unstated expectations. If that pushback connects with our own insecurities, even a simple comment can end up having quite a powerful effect. A girl who has been encouraged to be quiet and not make a fuss may find when she speaks out that she is told she is bossy. This might be enough to reinforce those previous, oft-repeated expectations, and she will quieten down again.

'The rules about what voice is allowed is a function of the community you are in,' Lucy Cornell explains. 'These rules are not ever written down and agreed upon, they are simply learned through assimilation and mimicry. In the West, the dominant vocal culture is still that of the white, alpha male. Anyone who is not that (male or female) needs to fight for their voice to be heard. Even if you are not part of that dominant culture, you still have the right to speak.'

You have the right to speak. The first step is acknowledging that. The next step is preparation, so that when you speak out a) you use your right to speak wisely, and b) you are ready for what follows.

Tips for rediscovering your voice

Many exercises for rediscovering your voice can be performed at home in your own time, to help put you in touch with your voice and vocal expression. Finding that connection is valuable for speaking out. Once you are more in touch with your voice (and 'inner voice', as described below), public speaking techniques will feel more natural and will come easier. Above all, remember that good communication comes from having *purpose*. The aim here is to free up your ability to breathe and function in a sometimes stressful public context while speaking with purpose – your purpose.

The following are some of Lucy's professional tips on how to rediscover and harness your voice, in her own words:

1. Trust your inner voice

Your inner voice is what drives you to speak – your gut instinct, your spirit, your beliefs. Before you speak out, the place to start is to find this inner voice. Your job is to find a way to connect with the content, to make it yours, to find a reason to speak it. This is the work of any performer – to tap into the inner strength that will keep them speaking with purpose. WHY are you speaking out? WHAT is driving it? Don't lose sight of that.

2. Let go, gain more

When speaking in high-stakes situations – such as in emotionally charged environments, or to people who have more power than you – paradoxically you have more control over your voice when you let go of:

- **Muscle holding**
  Become aware of the muscles in your body that habitually hold tension when you speak. For instance: your stomach, your throat, your pelvic floor, your jaw, your face etc. It is worth spending time becoming aware of your tension points. Only then do you have the option to consider the impact they have when you speak. Typically, unnecessary muscle tensions inhibit breath and ease in speaking. When you let go of some of these tensions your ability to respond is quicker and you will have more time to choose wiser thoughts.

- **Breath holding**
  There are numerous ways to hold your breath. For example: you may hold your breath before you speak, between your thoughts, or meter out your breath while you speak. Breath holding can give you a feeling of suspending time, which you secretly might want to do when you are in a situation you want to avoid, such as a confrontational conversation. However, this is a false feeling. Additionally, holding your breath gives your audience the impression that you are holding something back. So letting your breath go helps you regain control and be present to the reality of the conversation, while also helping your audience to relax and feel as though you have it all in hand.

- **Intellectual or emotional holding**

We all know the feeling of trying to remember someone's name when they are standing right in front of you. Under pressure it is difficult to recall, and yet the moment they walk away you remember it immediately. In the spotlight, the harder you try to recall information and the more emotionally worked up you get about it, the less accessible it often is. If you are able to give yourself a moment to think 'Ok, I'll just have to let that idea pass me by' – to let go of the idea – then invariably it will find its way back into the conversation. This requires an element of trust and commitment that the outcome you desire will happen.

- **Your attachment to the outcome**

Let's make a distinction between attachment and commitment. If you are attached to an outcome – getting what you want, being successful, sounding intelligent – then you have something to lose. Your ego is invested in it. Speaking is a moment by moment transaction and sometimes the conversation will go in a direction you do not plan. Being attached to an outcome blinds you to hearing what is needed in every moment. However, you do need to commit to your purpose – why you are here – to be open to what may come up and to respond to it. Letting go of your attachment to the journey you expected to take will help you stay present to what the conversation and your audience actually needs.

- **Trying to recreate a prepared moment**
  As every moment is different, it is unwise to think
  that what you rehearsed yesterday for this difficult
  conversation is what is going to eventuate in reality.
  Rehearsal is very effective, but the real conversation
  needs to be coupled with sharp listening, presence
  and response to what is required in every moment.

When you let go of anything that takes you away from
being present to each moment of speaking, you have time
to choose your words, and express yourself authentically.

Some common vocal issues for women

High pitch

High-pitched voices rely on the upper notes of the voice
and deny the deeper ones. In general women's voices are
anatomically higher in pitch than men's because of the
length of the vocal cords. However, that does not mean
that women do not have access to deeper notes.

For numerous cultural reasons, women sometimes
feel that it is not permissible to speak with depth
(as discussed earlier in the chapter). This myth is
disempowering for women. It means that many women
are not accessing their natural gravitas and authority.

Try this: Relaxation and deep, easy breathing are
the secrets to releasing the deeper notes of your voice.
Lie on the floor where you don't have to fight against

gravity and your own busy mind. Run through a simple relaxation exercise for 10 minutes, working from your toes to your head, gripping then ungripping each body part in turn. The relaxation that results will soften the muscles to do with breathing and release some of your unnecessary habitual tensions, which limit the vibrational capacity of your voice. Once you have let your body relax, test out your voice with a 'huh' sound a few times and then with a sigh of relief on sound: 'haaaa'. Notice where you feel vibrations in your body: chest, head, face, sacrum etc. Once you are aware of these vibrations, you can then focus your attention there with each sigh of relief: 'haaa', 'haaaa'. The premise is that the more relaxed you are the more deep vibrations you will find.

Rising inflection

This is when the voice rises in pitch at the end of a sentence, as though you are asking a question or reading out a list of ideas that you are ticking off in your head. It gives the impression that you are not certain of what you are saying, or committed to the value of your ideas.

Try this: The first step is awareness. Start by noting how many times you are doing it. Then find a time to practise the following techniques on your own or with a friend. Holding a book in your hand as you speak, bang it down on the desk as you reach the end of each phrase or sentence. Have your voice follow the energy of the book: direct and down. Notice the difference in your voice and the message when you do this.

Too quiet

Your voice will follow your intention. Sometimes you may not consciously intend to be quiet, but something woven into your survival psychology demands that of you. Speaking quietly can sometimes sound like you are speaking 'off your voice'. It sounds like you have removed the core energy and strength of your voice, and can seem a little breathy.

Try this: Lean your back against a wall, with your feet a couple of steps away from the wall, so that your back (from your buttocks to the top of your torso) is flat against the wall. Ensure you are breathing deeply. Press your weight into the wall and speak some words to the opposite wall, or out the window to people far away. Watch that you don't tense up in your neck, jaw or throat. Use your breath as the fuel to carry your voice. Each new thought that you speak needs to be preceded by a new breath.

You want to be careful that you are not just yelling. You have so many more dynamics available to you than just two modes, quiet and loud.

Vocal fry

(See earlier in the chapter for a description of what this is and how it is often perceived.)

Try this: The key is to breathe while relaxing your throat and larynx, the back of your tongue, and jaw. When there is not much breath, the muscles around the larynx have to work hard to get the voice out, hence the fry.

Start by lying on the floor and giving yourself 10 minutes to relax throughout your whole body and give over to gravity. (See the relaxation exercise on pages 67 to 68) Let your throat open, and relax the back of your tongue and jaw. Feed a deep, easy breath into your belly and release it on a sigh of relief, ensuring the channel through your throat and mouth relaxes open. Repeat and add voice, allowing your voice to be carried out by the breath. Think of your breath and voice as a wave moving in to shore. It doesn't push, it moves effortlessly. Remember, the deeper and easier the breath, the more relaxed the larynx muscles will be and the more easily the voice will come (minus the fry).

Projection

Projection often is interpreted as simply pushing your voice out. Be wary of the advice to 'Speak louder'. This will invariably cause you to push the voice by tensing your muscles, in order to reach a certain point or person. It sounds harsh and does not carry much depth or subtlety of feeling behind it. It lacks resonance.

Try this: True projection comes from combining resonance with intention. It is much more powerful and expressive to speak with a fully resonant voice without the tensions associated with trying to be heard. Rather than reaching or pushing your voice out with your head, neck, throat or jaw, ensure you use breath to support your voice. As you stand, let your body recall the feeling of relaxation from previous exercises. Imagine yourself in a tough conversation where you want to speak out. Check where your muscles tense up just in the imagining of that conversation. Now let them go. Breathe deeply and easily into your relaxed body. As the breath releases out, speak some of the words of this tough conversation as though you mean business. Be careful not to hold back your breath, push your voice or lean forward in your body. Stand your ground and speak with ease and your voice will have more resonance and more body to it. You will have more gravitas and impact.

To understand what resonance is in your voice, consider how resonance corresponds to an orchestra. The deepest notes of the orchestra, such as those of a tuba, are formed from large spaces and low breath energy. In your body, these deep notes of your voice ring in the large, bony space of your chest supported by a low-energy sigh.

The middle notes, much like those of the trumpet and horns, are higher in pitch. These middle notes of your voice ring in the smaller spaces of your mouth and teeth. They require more energised breath.

The higher notes of the orchestra come from narrower instruments such as the clarinet, flute and piccolo. The narrow chambers and cavities of your sinus and nose produce your upper notes and require a highly energised breath to support them.

The goal is to have your whole harmonic orchestra of notes playing through your voice, and to be on call to respond to the versatility of your thoughts and feelings.

Nerves

When you are really feeling nervous before a presentation, deep breathing helps to calm and centre you. This exercise will bring your heart, mind and body into one place.

Try this: Sit or stand calmly. Close your eyes.

Breathe all the air out of your lungs on a silent 'FFF', slowly and mindfully.

Once you feel your belly is empty of breath, let breath come in through your nose, slowly and mindfully.

Repeat this five times, aiming to lengthen the breath each time. Notice how your energy, mind and heart feel after this.

NOTE: The handy part of this technique is that you can do it the night before your presentation, in the wings on the day, or even in your seat in the audience before you go up to speak. It's silent and powerful.

Lucy Cornell is a professional voice coach with more than 15 years of global experience.

Using your diaphragm

...

Many voice coaches, athletes and spiritual teachers also recommend learning to use your diaphragm more efficiently. Here, briefly, is a rundown of what the diaphragm is, and how you can become more attuned to it.

Your diaphragm is a dome-shaped muscle below your ribcage and its downward and upward movement is vital for breathing. When you breathe in, your diaphragm contracts and pulls the lower part of the lungs downward, and you take in life-sustaining oxygen. When you exhale, the diaphragm and lungs relax and you expel carbon dioxide gas as waste. Learning to consciously activate your diaphragm and breathe from the belly rather than the chest is good for your health, your voice and your ability to remain calm while speaking in public.

Here is one simple exercise to get acquainted with your diaphragm, and to practise consciously activating it:

1. Lie on your back on the floor, with your knees slightly bent.
2. Place your hands gently on your stomach. Take some time to concentrate on your breathing, using your diaphragm (belly), not your chest.
3. Feel your tummy rise as your lungs fill from the bottom, then relax again.
4. Once you have felt your diaphragm at work in your breathing, stand up and, with your hands on your belly, try to continue to breathe and feel your diaphragm working.

Whether or not you decide to work on your voice, tone and breathing to improve the way you speak out, know that you deserve your time to speak out and be heard. Do your best to use it wisely.

CHAPTER 4

PUBLIC SPEAKING

Get ready!

...

Now that we have discussed some points relating to vocal expression, perceptions of the female voice and how to connect with or harness your individual public speaking voice through practice and exercises, let's talk about the other aspects of public speaking – namely how to prepare your speech and how to actually *do* it.

> It's not the end of the world, no matter what happens to you on stage.

Prepare, prepare, prepare

What works for me when preparing for public speeches is studying and prepping like my life depends on it, and then dropping all that tension before the talk and thinking, 'What the hell. Do your best. Failure's not the end of the world.' It's *not* the end of the world, no matter what happens to you on stage. Your talk will not trigger the apocalypse, and despite the feeling many people get before speaking in public, only rarely does a single speech make a difference to your entire life. We can put far too much pressure on ourselves in the moment. Even if the topiaries wilt and the audience doesn't speak to you for a while, as I relayed in my story earlier, you will be fine. As rare as such an occurrence is, if it happens to you, you will be okay. You will go on to speak another day, to another audience.

Prepare, prepare, prepare, and then let go of the outcome.

After a couple of decades of experience I now have a pretty good sense of just how much preparation I need, and I tend to feel best when I over-prepare. (Within reason. As a full-time working parent and part-time PhD student I don't have loads of spare time.) What I want to avoid is a feeling, just before going on, that I am not sure if I know what I want to say. I want to be totally connected with my

message, and well prepared for any
questions or criticism about it.
In other words, I need to have
looked at the issue from many
angles, and I need to be certain
about what I am going to say.

> When my argument feels solid, and I
> am well connected with that message,
> I feel ready.

When my argument feels solid, and I am well connected with that
message, I feel ready.

Use your voice well

Once you have your message, you will again need to make sure
you are in touch with your voice (see the previous chapter) so that
you are using your own best possible voice when you are speaking
out publicly. This takes some conscious preparation and practice,
but anyone can do it. Just as singers warm up their voices before
performing, you may find vocal practice in a private room just before
you speak helps you to get in the right frame before your speech. I
often (but not always) slip away to a side room or dressing room for
five minutes to run through my opening lines just before I get on
stage. Many speakers and performers do this, and it may work for
you, to bring focus and to loosen up your voice.

Stick to your speech

If you prepare beforehand and know your stuff (see **Chapter 5**),
speak that truth and don't worry too much what others think. There
will be folded arms in that room, as well as applause. You can't please
them all, but you can communicate things that matter. Second
thoughts part-way through can lead you to feel uncertain or even
go off course. Don't abandon what you have to say. Try to stick to
your plan and remember that you are thoroughly prepared and your
material is good.

If you can, speak without reading from notes

Jane Gilmore, writer and former editor of website *Women's Agenda*, wrote the following about me in October 2015:

> I went to a Business Chicks breakfast a few months back where Tara Moss spoke for 45 minutes. She had no podium, no notes and used the screens only to show a few photos and a couple of graphs. She didn't skip a beat the whole time and it was one of the most engaging public addresses I'd ever heard. I assumed this was something that just came naturally to her, but she told me afterwards that she had taught herself to do it as a means of overcoming nerves about speaking in public …

This *is* something you can learn and master. Jane went on to describe how she used the same techniques to achieve the ability to speak without notes:

> It does require a lot of preparation in the beginning. I still write a full speech a few days before the event, and practice it out loud to my dogs to check the timing and flow. Then I read it over and over again until I've got it mostly memorised. I also do a dot point summary to put in my phone and keep it in my pocket as a safety net, but I think just having it there means I don't panic and draw a total blank – I've not yet had to use it. When you've done that amount of preparation you're much less likely to be nervous and once you start speaking, it's surprising how easily you fall into the rhythms you've already practiced. Also, if you're not looking at notes or a screen you're making direct contact with the audience, which make[s] you much more engaging and them much more interested.[1]

While I can't claim that I have time to master *every* speech in this way before taking to the stage, I certainly aim to. I find this is particularly effective for large audiences, and for speeches on subjects I speak about often, so I can repeat parts of those speeches in the future. Again, the best way to avoid drawing a blank or sounding uncertain is to have *purpose*. If everything you plan to say has purpose and is logically necessary for your argument, you are less likely to feel lost on stage, or to appear unsure.

If you're not looking at notes or a screen you're making direct contact with the audience, which make[s] you much more engaging and them much more interested.

JANE GILMORE, WRITER

How to speak without notes

Here is my method for speaking without notes, in four basic steps:

1. **Write your speech out first.** Identify what you want to say in parts or sections that can be remembered. Your first written version may be lengthy if, like me, you like to work out your arguments thoroughly beforehand until your central points become clear.

2. **Look at the way the sections of your speech link up.** What is the overall format? Is it telling a story chronologically? Is it starting with describing a problem and ending with offering a solution? Decide if the content is arranged in the most effective order.

3. **Find a way to memorise the link points.** What leads to what? Ideally, when you finish one section you will know what comes next, and it will roll on seamlessly. To assist with this, you can also use PowerPoint slides as prompts or have a piece of paper with bullet points as a backup.

4. **Practise.** Along with crafting the message you want, practising is the most important part of speaking confidently without notes. Do it at home. Do it in an empty room, in front of your pets, your loved ones, whoever will listen. It may feel uncomfortable talking aloud to an empty room, or having your friend sit through your speech, but the more you practise, the less likely you will be to feel unprepared, and therefore nervous.

You deserve your time to speak

You deserve to speak out. Do your best to use it wisely. Prepare well, dedicate time to thoughtfully considering and honing your message (including any corrections or changes when better information comes to light). And then, knowing your message, speak out and share that message with confidence.

There will be folded arms in that room, as well as applause. You can't please them all, but you can communicate things that matter.

You've got this.

CHAPTER 5

WRITING

> '**Writing, in its noblest function,
> is the attempt to unerase,
> to unearth ...**'
> HÉLÈNE CIXOUS[1]

The written word can be incredibly powerful for articulating (or *unearthing, unerasing,* to paraphrase Cixous) important information, perspectives, stories and histories. Good examples of writing, whether fiction or non-fiction, short or long, can have great impact and longevity. Just think of a book that changed your childhood, or a news report that altered your view of the world. Make no mistake, written words can be powerful.

Some of you may find your voices primarily through writing – as professional authors, journalists, opinion writers or academics – while others will complement different lives, careers and forms of public participation with things like blogging, essays, social media posts and more. Regardless of the genre or medium, making your words count is a valuable skill, and has become increasingly important now that so much of our speaking out and communication with the world happens digitally and online (see **chapters 12 and 13**). The digital age has made nearly all of us 'publishers' of content, making most of us writers in ways that, a decade or so ago, did not exist. Even those who would never consider themselves 'authors' are now precisely that, publishing their writings, sometimes several times a day, to some size of audience, whether it be friends on social media or millions of readers.

> The digital age has made nearly all of us 'publishers' of content, making most of us writers in ways that, a decade or so ago, did not exist.

With writing, as with speaking, content is key. In other parts of this book (**chapter 6**), we explore how to form an argument, how to research, find good sources and avoid publicly using incorrect data or factual inaccuracies. In this chapter, however, we will focus on some of the essentials of the writing craft itself.

My golden rules for writing

...

How does one not only write, but write well?

As a writer I have often grappled with this question. Style varies a great deal from writer to writer, and from context to context, but there are certain elements most good writing shares.

Make your words count

It is important to not simply *use* words, but to have a reason for employing them. Think of any writing project, be it an email, essay or book, as having a 'budget'. This is not a financial budget, but a budget on words and time – your time, sure, but most importantly you reader's time (and if you have one, your editor's time). If a sentence does not forward your argument or your story, cut it out. Avoid using several words to articulate something when one will do just as well.

> If someone requests an 800-word article, they have room for 800 words, not 1800.

Check each sentence for relevance and clarity. If it doesn't pass muster, re-word it or cut it.

If you find that several sentences say the same thing in different ways, cut back that point or explanation to its clearest, most succinct form. Some subtle or complex ideas may need to be articulated in several ways to be clear, and some points can be repeated for emphasis, but as a general rule, saying the same thing in different ways can be wasteful and offputting for readers. Take the red pen or delete button to any repetition that is unnecessary.

Thankfully, a lot of this culling can be done in the editing process, so don't worry too much if you find you need to 'write it out' in order to let the ideas flow initially. In that case don't aim to write it right, make it right later in editing. But even knowing you will edit your writing, it is still good to keep your aim of being concise in mind as you write.

Making your words count means checking the literal meaning of sentences, avoiding unnecessary repetitions and making sure each sentence in some way progresses your argument or story.

Be conscious of word count

Further to the above, 'word count' is something with which many writers will become intimately familiar. No writer, regardless of genre, has an infinite amount of time and publication space. Likewise, one word does not a story make, though it is possible to tell a heart-wrenching story in just six:

> For sale: Baby shoes. Never worn.[2]

This shortest of short stories is often attributed to Ernest Hemingway, who reportedly won a 10 dollar wager that he could write a six-word story with a beginning, middle and end (we'll look briefly at standard structure below), though the actual source of this famous story is disputed.[3] You see, it's not about how many words you use, it's how you use them. 'It wasn't by accident', wrote Hemingway, 'that the Gettysburg address was so short.'[4] That said, the length of a work must suit the story, argument, and the 'size', if you will, of what the author has to say, or the publication space the author has been given, whether it is six words, 600 or 160,000. It needs to 'fit'. As a writer's experience grows, the general word count or word 'budget' that a story or idea needs becomes something you can sense, and for some writers, like myself, mapping this progress becomes part of the writing process.

For example, when writing a book or other long-form project that will take months or years, I will know the general length I am aiming for. This is based on the 'size' and scope of what I want to say, and my sense as an experienced writer as to how much space the idea needs. I will then often check the word count as I write, even going so far as to log a daily word count to monitor my progress towards a deadline. (If using Word, go to the Tools tab, and scroll down to Word Count. If using software like Scrivener, you can set word count goals and deadlines, and monitor your progress.) This can help to keep me disciplined on a project that might need to be realised over 100,000 words or more. When writing shorter essays or opinion pieces I don't keep a log, but I do need to keep within a set word limit, and this provides another reason to keep an eye on my word 'budget'.

Not sure what length you should be aiming for? Here are some general guidelines:

• Articles, essays, opinion pieces

Any person writing for publications will quickly find that word count parameters are quite real. If someone requests an 800-word article, they have room for 800 words, not 1800. If what you send them is more than 10% over the word count allotment they have, they will be required to cut your piece down. You don't want that. Try to be economical with your words, keep the commissioned or projected length in mind when you begin the writing, and try to edit the piece down to your own satisfaction before submitting, keeping to within 10% of the limit, as a general rule. Sending a little more is better than sending something under the given limit, but keep in mind that publications will often cut a piece to almost precisely the word limit that was set, regardless of how important you deem those other words of yours to be.

• Books

You initially have a lot more scope for word count when writing a book, and you may not have to keep length in mind at all, but most authors will tell you how unwieldy a work can become if you forget about projected length entirely and allow your work to wander. Good books vary in length – most of mine are 90,000 to 120,000 words, for example, and many authors write to very different lengths – but if your work becomes extremely long, all those pages had better be worth it. An epic fiction story or comprehensive book or PhD will logically take many more pages to do its job than short fiction or an essay. Regardless of length, try to keep the work tight. Make each page or chapter count.

If you are unsure about the length you should be aiming for, get an idea of the length of the books you like, or the length of books that are comparable to what you hope to achieve, and use that as a general guideline.

• Blogs and social media

Some social media platforms, like Twitter, make meandering all but impossible by keeping you to a 140 character limit. Other platforms have different limits. As a rule, short posts get shared the most.[5] In fact, the optimal length for a tweet is 71–100 characters, while the optimal Facebook post length is apparently only 40 characters, despite the fact that you are given far more room. As a writer I find that somewhat depressing, but it can guide you as to the best medium to use when articulating what you have to say.

Some 'long' posts on social media can be very effective, but even that is usually no more than 250 words. Generally speaking, if you want space to make a point, you may be looking at writing a blog, which you can then share on social media. Blogs are usually considered best if they contain a minimum of 300 words and less than 1000. If you are publishing something more comprehensive, it will generally be viewed as a 'long read', and will need to be between 1200 and 5000 words. About seven minutes' reading time, or 1600 words, is deemed 'optimal' for a blog, according to data put together by Medium,[6] though views on this differ.

Again, as with all writing, it's not what you have, word length-wise, but what you do with it. A powerful, tightly written 5000-word post that some people deem too long to read online may be far more important to get out there than an easily digested and frequently shared 500-word post. My blogs tend to be on the long side – for example my most read and shared post, 'Manus Island – an insider's report',[7] which won an award for Outstanding Advocacy, is about 3500 words in length. I publish blogs perhaps once or twice a month, while other writers publish regular, shorter blogs weekly or even daily. Both approaches can be effective, depending on your natural writing style, what you are trying to convey, or what you ultimately hope to achieve with your writing. Through practice you will quickly discover which lengths come more naturally for you, and best suit your subject and audience.

Part-way through the writing, if you realise you have a lot more to say than you thought or that your point is actually bigger or more significant that you first sensed, you may be able to change your chosen publication medium (unless it is a commissioned article, for example) to suit the piece that you want to write. Perhaps you started out writing a simple response to something on social media but you realise, as you are typing, that you actually have more to say than you thought. That's good. Go with it. Give yourself the time and space to write with more depth on the subject. Listen to that instinct, and go with the subjects and stories that compel you.

Avoid unnecessary repetition

Further to the first point on making your words count, you should avoid unnecessary repetitions of not only sentences and concepts, but vocabulary and syntax. As a rule, apart from frequently used words like *a, the, with*, and so on, you should avoid repeating the same words in close proximity. Exceptions to this rule include intentional repetition for necessary emphasis or linguistic play, or in dialogue to reflect the way a character or interviewee speaks. However, if you use a descriptor like 'unfortunately', in one sentence, for example, make sure you don't use it again soon after. It can be easy to get into a pattern of using the same phrases and words in your work, without intending to. Be sure to check for this when you re-read your work and change any repetitions where they are unintentional.

Don't write it right, just write it and make it right later

As you may have noticed already, the beauty of a lot of writing is that you can take time, whether it is hours, days or years (in the case of books, PhDs etc), to make it right. Writing is not often an instantaneous creation, and that allows you to be more precise than you might be while speaking. Take advantage of that difference by using the time you have to make your points well. Particularly if your piece is 500 words and over, it often pays to sit on it overnight and read again with fresh eyes in the morning. If deadlines prevent this, try reading it to someone else, or even reading it aloud to yourself. This process can sometimes illuminate previously hidden errors. If writing anxiety affects you, it can be helpful to keep the safety net of this editing process firmly in mind. Give yourself permission to freely write what comes, and worry about whether it works when you are ready to re-read and edit.

When you are writing it you need to feel that it matters.

Do a final re-read

Never publish or send anything without re-reading it. This is obvious, but I really do mean *never*. Whether it is a two word text, a tweet, letter or book chapter you've been pouring over for weeks, never press send, post or publish until you re-read what you actually have on the page. Yes, we can all make mistakes and I have made plenty of typos, but this simple step of re-reading what you wrote (or ended up with after auto-correct etc) goes a long way towards avoiding unnecessary and perhaps potentially disastrous errors.

> Never publish or send anything without re-reading it. This is obvious, but I really do mean *never*.

Think of your readers

We can all write diaries and personal reflections for ourselves – in fact I think this is a very healthy although dying art form. However, when speaking out through writing, you are writing with the intention of the work being read by others. Think about your audience. For many writers, the first draft is about themselves – letting the words and ideas flow. This can be a good way to get the ideas on the page initially. The edit, however, is about the future readers of that work. To reiterate points made above, you should think about your readers when you consider: Am I being clear? Am I using words wisely? Am I being succinct, i.e., not wasting words as I tell my story or make my point? Do I *have* a point?

Stephen King's autobiography *On Writing* is, in my view, one of the best books on the subject, and though it obviously focuses on fiction more than non-fiction, the advice he recounts from his early career, given to him by an editor named John Gould, is timeless and helpful for any writer, regardless of the genre or medium of their writing:

'When you write a story, you're telling yourself the story,' he [Gould] said. 'When you rewrite, your main job is taking out all the things that are *not* the story.'[8]

This is a good general philosophy for approaching any writing, including storytelling, but also non-fiction or 'argument essay' writing. Once you know your argument, your purpose or your story, your job in the editing or rewriting is to take out everything that is not contributing to it. Meandering ideas and frequent sidetrips to other issues do not make for good or persuasive writing. You will lose your reader.

I apply this philosophy to both my fiction and non-fiction writing. Before I publish anything or submit any writing to a publisher, I try to read it as another reader would. Does it make sense? Does it grab me? Have I gone off on a tangent? Is there anywhere I can trim it back without losing vital elements of my story or argument?

Conversely, you will want to try to read your work as a stranger to be sure you have actually written what you intended. As the writer, you generally know more about your intention, your chosen subject or story than your readers, and because of this you can sometimes fail to include vital information. You may not notice it is missing, because it's in your head and you fill in the blanks when you re-read the work, seeing what is not yet on the page. With that in mind, think of your readers and *make sure what you are trying to write is on the page.*

> Once you know your argument, your purpose or your story, your job in the editing or rewriting is to take out everything that is not contributing to it.

How to improve your writing

...

Read

The first step towards good writing is good reading. Read widely and read often. Because many of you will speak out on particular topics, be sure to read widely on those topics, as well as other topics that provide greater world context. Read books, news articles and (good) blogs. This will help you to develop not only a better understanding of your subject, but will help you to become a better writer. If you want to write well, study what writing well looks like. Read critically. Reflect on how the writer is achieving their aim. There is no substitute for this.

Write

One of the most important things you can do to hone your writing abilities is simply to write. No amount of study and thinking/over-thinking the writing process can replace the value of practice.

> It is ultimately writing that makes you a writer, nothing else.

I often recommend that new writers try to write something each day (but not necessarily publish anything, until they are ready). Most find their comfort with writing and their skills improve rapidly with daily practice, whether it is just 20 minutes a day or something more substantial. As an example, you could try writing 100 (edited) words of a story or non-fiction book each day, and in about two years you would have a full-length book. When I am writing a book I aim for 1000 words a day during the majority of the intensive writing process, though the actual word count varies enormously in practice (from a measly 100 words on terrible days to 5000 or more words on days when the words and ideas really flow). Setting daily, or at least regular, word count or writing time goals can help you get going. This takes discipline.

A significant amount of the writing process involves research, plotting or structuring, and editing, rather than actual writing, but getting some words on the page regularly can help prevent stagnation or the dreaded 'writer's block', and writing regularly is one sure way to improve your skills and create a body of work. In short, it is ultimately writing that makes you a writer, nothing else.

Hone your vocabulary, grammar and spelling

The most essential tool for writing is language. Without it, you can't articulate your ideas. To write effectively you are going to want a good grasp of the vocabulary of both your chosen language and your chosen writing subject, and you are going to want to employ correct spelling whenever possible. We all make typos, of course, but doing this often looks sloppy, is distracting, and may completely change the meaning of your sentences.

Good grammar matters. Spelling out the principles of grammar (or indeed, providing a dictionary) is not within the scope of this book, but if you know your grammar is wanting, it's good to acknowledge that and do something about it. There are excellent books on grammar, and writing courses are also available in many cities, as well as online.

Thankfully your vocabulary, grammar and sense of writing will improve with reading (the first step, as mentioned above), so don't waste that opportunity – read the good stuff. Further, get a dictionary if you don't already have one (digital or printed), get a thesaurus, and use them.

Study structure

Whether it be an argument essay or a fiction novel, structure is a vital element of all writing. The classic structure is usually thought of as having three parts – a beginning, middle and end, a tripartite structure first articulated in Aristotle's *Poetics*, a text from around 335 BC. Like most rules, the rules of structure can be broken, but if they are it must be handled very well. To knowingly break with established structure is very different from departing from structural conventions due to ignorance of them. If you are new to writing, I strongly suggest studying standard structure before deciding that such conventions do not apply to your work.

If you want to know what this looks like, study the structure of classic writing. Can you identify where the writer offers their starting argument or where they set up the plot? That is the beginning, or Part 1. Can you see how the pace or argument flows through the middle? That's Part 2. Can you pinpoint the finale or conclusion? Voila, there is Part 3.

Here is an idea of what a piece of persuasive non-fiction writing should include:

1. An introduction to the topic, and if relevant, a thesis statement, or statement of opinion.
2. Facts relating to the topic. This can include information from credible sources, like statistics, prevalence, etc.
3. Acknowledge and if possible disprove any opponents' arguments on the topic.
4. Prove your own argument on the topic.
5. Make a concluding statement.

In this instance, points 3 and 4, or 2, 3 and 4, may all be seen as belonging to the 'middle' or second part, with the introduction (point 1) and ending (point 5) providing parts 1 and 3 respectively. This structure is simple and can be applied to many types of non-fiction writing of different lengths. If you can introduce your topic or premise, state the facts, debate issues relating to the topic and offer some conclusions, you have a standard structure in place. Though it is generally a good idea to take a little more time to prove an argument, in a short work this may be as simple as a three paragraph argument, with an introduction to your argument, a further fleshing out of that argument and a concluding paragraph.

And finally, do not 'come lightly to the blank page'

Just as I wrote in the previous chapter – that in order to get on that stage and expect others to listen, you have to have something to say – to write and expect others to read your work, your writing needs substance and purpose. When you are writing it, you need to feel that it *matters*. It can matter like a movie review or a short fiction, or it can matter like a political manifesto or a report on an atrocity, but it still has to matter. It has to *be something* to you. To again quote King:

> You can approach the act of writing with nervousness, excitement, hopefulness, or even despair – the sense that you can never quite put on the page what's in your heart. You can come to the act with your fists clenched and your eyes narrowed, ready to kick ass and take down names. You can come to it because you want a girl to marry you or because you want to change the world. Come to it any way but lightly. Let me say it again: *you must not come lightly to the blank page.*[9]

Write. Be read. Make your voice heard. But do not come lightly to the page (or the podium). Take the time to know why you are doing this, and what you have to say. Only then will you be using your words wisely.

Writing checklist

- Have I re-read my work?

- Have I checked my spelling and grammar?

- Is there a beginning, middle and end, or some other functioning structure in place?

- Have I checked each sentence for literal meaning, clarity and relevance?

- Is the purpose or story clear?

- How might I be misinterpreted? (If there is a way to fix any possible misinterpretations, do it.)

- If there is a word count limit, am I within 10% of my projected/commissioned word count? (If not, check what you can cut back, or re-think your publication medium.)

- Have I re-read it again? (For some, doing this out loud is best, to 'hear' any mistakes.)

Further reading

A single chapter cannot possibly hope to cover more than the bare essentials of the writing process. For further reading:

Argue, persuade and advise, www.bbc.co.uk/bitesize/ks3/english/writing/argue_persuade_advise/revision/1/

Joe Landsberger (undated), 'Persuasive or argumentative essays', Study Guides and Strategies, Writing assignments series

Stephen King, *On Writing*, Scribner, New York, 2000

Anne Lamott, *Bird by Bird: Some Instructions on Writing and Life*, Anchor Books, New York, 1995

William Strunk Jr and E.B. White, *Elements of Style*, numerous publishers and editions

CHAPTER 6

KNOWING YOUR STUFF

Get informed

...

The better informed we are before we speak out, the more we are able to positively contribute when we do, and the more reason there'll be for people to listen.

This can't be stressed enough, and so in this chapter we will delve into that aspect of speaking out in further detail. Knowing your stuff is not only important for your own understanding of the issues, your integrity, confidence and experience of speaking out (including any consequences of your speaking out, as we will discuss), but it is also important on an ethical level. It is important for your audience or readership that you are not spreading misinformation, and that is, in my view, one of the responsibilities of speaking out. Not everyone will agree with your opinions, but your factual statements should be accurate and properly attributed. When you quote someone, that quote should be accurate. When you use statistics or facts – and don't be afraid to use them, they are valuable – they should be correctly represented and attributed. If you present facts that do not have factual backing, you are spreading misinformation (like that scientific-sounding pronouncement that women use 20,000 words per day and their male counterparts just 7000, as we heard earlier). No one is perfect, but there are ways to avoid certain mistakes, and when you do, it is better for everyone.

Knowing your stuff matters whether you are speaking out in a speech, interview, book, blog, social media post or meme.

Only you can know what topic you will choose to speak out on, and why, and you and you alone will ultimately have the responsibility of researching that area so you know your stuff. However, in this chapter I will explore a few things that every person speaking out should consider carefully.

Critical thinking

...

In order to know your stuff, you will need to be sure you have put your critical thinking cap on. What do I mean by this? The Critical Thinking – Concepts and Tools mini-guide by Dr Richard Paul and Dr Linda Elder describes critical thinking as 'the art of analysing and evaluating thinking with a view to improving it.'[1] Or to put it another way, 'Critical thinking is thinking about your thinking, while you're thinking, in order to make your thinking better.'

The opposite of critical thinking is lazy thinking, when we fail to challenge our biases, examine what we think we know and why we think we know it. Left unexamined, our thinking can be distorted and our belief systems can be fundamentally wrong, and therefore easily debunked when aired publicly. As Dr Steven Novella, an academic clinical neurologist at Yale University School of Medicine, writes, 'for an argument to be sound all of its premises must be true. Often, different people come to different conclusions because they are starting with different premises. So examining all the premises of each argument is a good place to start.'[2] That is better for you, and it is better for your readers or audience as well.

You will want to analyse your premise and your own thinking when forming and honing your argument. You will need to question why you think what you think, before sharing it. Critical thinking is a strong focus of most academic institutions, but it is something every person can learn regardless of their exposure to those environments, and this is an area where I recommend that you do some further reading. (You can start with something like the mini-guide mentioned above, at www.criticalthinking.org/files/Concepts_Tools.pdf, and look further.)

When you are engaged in critical thinking, you are considering your arguments from all angles, gathering and assessing relevant information as fairly as possible, and taking the time to be sure you are using any stats, quotes and other information correctly.

Among your self-assessments when forming your argument, make sure you ask yourself the following questions:

You may still have critics - in fact almost everyone does have critics - but they won't be able to dismiss you or your argument by pointing out that you got your facts wrong.

1. What is my view on the topic I will speak out on (through my writing, speaking etc) and why do I hold that view?

a) Where did I get my ideas? Can I trace the source?

b) Are the sources of my information reliable? If not, look for new sources now. (More on sources shortly.)

c) If my views are formed purely from personal experience, have I looked elsewhere to see if this is experienced by others? What information is out there? What is the wider context? Are my personal perceptions reliable in this case or could they be distorted for any reason?

d) Have I looked for other sources of information on the topic? If not, start now.

2. Have I tested my views? Do they hold up to scrutiny?

a) What might criticism of my views look like?

b) Where is my argument weakest?

c) What other views are held on the topic? Have I fairly examined and considered those views?

d) What reliable, documented history, studies or information can I use to back up my argument? (Or debunk it, in which case you may wish to strongly consider changing your argument.)

e) Is there any aspect of my argument that I have not verified, questioned or tested?

3. Do I use a mixture of fact and opinion in my argument, and if so, have I examined both the opinions and the facts I am using to forward my argument?

a) Have I questioned my statements? Am I sure about them?

b) Are the opinions I hold backed up by the facts I am presenting?

c) Are there other relevant facts I am dismissing? If so, why?

4. When communicating my argument, am I being clear?

a) Do I give examples?

b) Do I provide context?

c) Is my argument balanced, while also providing a clear point and having purpose?

d) Where possible, do I provide citations or links to further information? (For example, to data from the World Health Organization, the Australian Bureau of Statistics, to experts or credible organisations etc?)

Considering each of these issues and possibilities will help make your argument more solid and lend it depth and help you avoid the pitfalls of publicly getting factual information wrong, both for you and your intended audience.

What else should you be considering?

Quoting other people

...

When making an argument and/or speaking out, you may find it is helpful to quote others. After all, our arguments are rarely formed in total isolation – they stem from past discoveries and ideas, and are influenced by current discoveries and ideas. Because the work of others can be valuable to our own, it stands to reason that those other thinkers are acknowledged, and any quotes from them are attributed correctly.

Do you know that saying about how 'It is easier to ask forgiveness than it is to get permission'? If you look online you'll see variations on this quote, including one by US entrepreneur Mark Suster: 'It's better to beg forgiveness than to ask for permission.' You can even get that on a canvas for your wall, if you're into that sort of thing.

But is it actually Mark's saying, or was he simply repeating a version of something much older? A bit of research will tell you that the late Rear Admiral Grace Hopper[2] said it is 'easier to ask forgiveness than it is to get permission' in a 1986 interview. She was a very accomplished woman, and at the time of her retirement was the oldest serving officer in the US Navy. So is that where it ends? Actually, no. Hopper's words from the interview stem from an old Jesuit credo – and so the quote trail goes on ...

Now, perhaps it doesn't particularly matter to you who originally said this, but if you do want to use a quote when you speak out, you will want to attribute that quote to the correct source. This is just one aspect of 'knowing your stuff', as we'll see, but it can be an important one. Knowing your stuff and getting the details right may take a few minutes, or it may take days, weeks or years. (Sorry. That's what PhDs are about. Some questions aren't easily or speedily answered.) Often it doesn't take a lot longer to know your stuff – at least the basics – than it does to make an error. Do what you can to get it right. It matters.

For example, actor and activist Mark Ruffalo posted a quote on his Tumblr page on 26 March 2015 that went viral. It was a perfect smack-down of the 'I am not a feminist' internet phenomenon, and news agencies and gossip columns reported it around the world. In June 2015, News Ltd quoted it word for word under the headline 'Mark Ruffalo on the "I am not a feminist internet phenomenon"', writing:

> Here's what he [Mark Ruffalo] said ... 'You're insulting every woman who was forcibly restrained in a jail cell with a feeding tube down her throat for your right to vote, less than 100 years ago.
>
> 'You're degrading every woman who has accessed a rape crisis centre, which wouldn't exist without the feminist movement.
>
> 'You're undermining every woman who fought to make marital rape a crime (it was legal until 1993).
>
> 'You're spitting on the legacy of every woman who fought for women to be allowed to own property (1848). For the abolition of slavery and the rise of the labor union. For the right to divorce. For women to be allowed to have access to birth control (Comstock laws). For middle and upper class women to be allowed to work outside the home (poor women have always worked outside the home). To make domestic violence a crime in the US (It is very much legal in many parts of the world). To make workplace sexual harassment a crime.
>
> 'In short, you know not what you speak of. You reap the rewards of these women's sacrifices every day of your life. When you grin with your [cutesy] sign about how you're not a feminist, you ignorantly spit on the sacred struggle of the past 200 years. You bite the hand that has fed you freedom, safety, and a voice.
>
> 'In short, kiss my ass, you ignorant little jerks.'[3]

Now, this is a good quote because the argument is excellent and the history quoted in it is well researched. The rights of women to vote, to own and have control over their own earnings and property, to be able to divorce and access birth control and more, are all things the feminist movement has been responsible for, along with introducing rape crisis centres and campaigning against child labour. All this can be easy to forget when some people are so fond of throwing the word 'feminazi' around. (Because apparently fighting for human rights is almost exactly like the Holocaust?)

Yes, this quote is a good one and pretty darn worthy of republishing.

The problem is, Ruffalo didn't say or write this, he *shared* it. The quote is from Tumblr blogger Libby Anne Bruce, from July 2014.[4] Ruffalo attributed it to her when he posted it, but everyone else ignored that, excited as they were by the idea that a famous male actor would say such spot-on things about feminism. There are now memes (loosely defined as images or video clips, often with text over the top, that are shared on the internet; in this case Libby Anne's words printed over images of Mark Ruffalo's face and shared widely) all over the web with Libby Anne's words attributed to Mark Ruffalo. I've even listened to some excellent people give speeches that included parts of this quote, again with the wrong attribution. It's easy to do because it is misattributed all over the place, and Ruffalo is known to be an activist, so it is easy enough to believe he'd say it.

Interestingly, in many instances you may begin to research something and find that women have said or done things, only to have their quotes, achievements, inventions and more attributed to famous men. This is a common issue, and something to avoid participating in wherever possible. It is certainly ironic that it happened to Libby Anne Bruce in relation to a quote about feminism – a movement that aims to lessen this ongoing problem of failing to recognise women's contributions in favour of men's (along with other important issues). I've fallen prey to this myself when I haven't done my research.

As another quick example, Voltaire did not say, 'I disapprove of what you say, but I will defend to the death your right to say it', though he is frequently misquoted as having said it. It was actually in Evelyn Beatrice Hall's 1906 biography of Voltaire, in which she wrote: '"I disapprove of what you say, but I will defend to the death your right to say it," was his attitude now.'[5] She was explaining his position, not quoting him directly. Her turn of phrase in explaining Voltaire's philosophy became a viral quote *by* Voltaire. I think I might even have misattributed her quote in a school paper once. It's easy to do.

Get your facts right
...

In public life there is essentially very little *forgiveness*, especially now that so many of our statements are recorded online for all to see, searchable into infinity. It is easier to seek the correct information than ask forgiveness once you have made an incorrect public statement. You don't want to speak out and be demonstrably wrong. That is spreading misinformation – it isn't good for your credibility and may even end up being quite unpleasant for you, or others.

The way to prevent that from happening is to know your stuff, as much as it is possible to. You may still have critics – in fact almost everyone *does* have critics – but they won't be able to dismiss you or your argument by pointing out that you got your facts wrong. So even if you have a pressing deadline, make sure you

> In public life there is essentially very little forgiveness, especially now that so many of our statements are recorded online for all to see, searchable into infinity.

do the best you can to know your stuff before you make that speech in public, post that blog or even make that social media update (it's unlikely, but it could in fact go viral and be in your life forever).

How you correctly attribute quotes is not the only thing you need to know before you speak out. You also need to get your concepts right, your stats right, your history right and more. A lot of this requires the same basic research techniques.

Seek information first. Ask questions. This is something I have learned time and time again. I don't always get it right, but I am now extremely motivated to try. I want you to be motivated too. The better informed we are before we speak out, the more we are able to positively contribute when we do, and the more reason there'll be for people to listen.

Know your stuff: Checklist
...

If you are going to speak out publicly, whether on a stage or in a blog, know your stuff first. Asking yourself these simple questions will help:

1. Is there an existing body of literature on my topic?

Yes? Excellent. Read as much of it as you reasonably can, focusing particularly on the prominent texts, arguments and positions, even if it is only with a view to refuting the ideas presented. By knowing what has already been written or said on a topic, you will know what criticism to expect when you speak out about it. (See PART THREE: WHAT TO EXPECT WHEN YOU SPEAK OUT.) You can prepare for likely counter-arguments (see question 3 below) and feel more confident of your position. And in the process of reading the existing knowledge base you will considerably expand your own.

Delve into the past, and follow the arguments right up to the present. Take the time to do it. This is how the best arguments are formed.

Keep in mind that most people speaking out will become associated with particular issues, ideas or areas of knowledge. You don't need to be an expert in everything (in fact, no one is), but you should do your best to be well versed in the area you choose to speak out on.

2. Am I applying critical thinking?

We've mentioned critical thinking already, and it is worth mentioning it again. Go through your critical thinking checklist.

I do despair when I hear some people blankly decry academia as meaningless and disconnected from the rest of the world, because much of academia is precisely about critical thinking, as well as awareness of historical context. And not all academics live in 'ivory towers'. Many of them also work in the fields they write in. (And besides, ivory is illegal.) Don't be afraid of reading academic work.

Once you have looked at the relevant writing on the subject, ask yourself what you think about your topic, as objectively as possible. Don't be discouraged if the topic is not as straightforward as you first thought. That is a sign that you now know your stuff better. Apply critical thinking to your arguments and don't be afraid to change your own mind before you set about changing the minds of others by speaking out.

3. What are the likely counter-arguments?

Hopefully, by reading the existing body of literature on your chosen topic, you have familiarised yourself with what has been said and by whom, and you should have a pretty good idea of some likely counter-arguments. List them.

If you haven't yet come across counter-arguments it is worth setting your mind to what counter-arguments there might be. For example, before you did your research, what did you think about the topic? How did the new information change your view, if at all? Are there common misconceptions about the topic? List those and think of how you might respond to them. (Also see **Chapter 7: Handling Criticism**.)

4. Are my sources credible?

This is an incredibly important point, not only for your own understanding of any given topic, but also for your credibility when speaking out. Always check that your information is coming from credible sources (see box, **Finding credible sources**, on pages 113 to 119). You don't want to leave 'digital fingerprints' all over the web, where false or offensive statements are attributed to your name. And you don't want to be submitting arguments quoting some debunked theory, or an extreme right-wing self-proclaimed 'conspiracy theorist' from Texas. Nor do you want to be misattributing quotes to wonderful actors who nonetheless didn't say them. Check your quotes and check out the people you choose to quote. Check your sources and your data. Everyone may have the right to free speech, but not everyone is right and not everything you read is right. No one gets it right all the time, but do the work to get it as right as possible as often as possible.

Finding credible sources

Here are some tips on how to find credible sources of information:

Check your sources

Let's say you've found a statistic or quote that works, and if it's a quote, you're satisfied that you've attributed it to the correct person. The next step is to check the source itself for credibility. Do they have any professional affiliation with the subject? Are they an expert? If so, what makes them an expert? Is your source known for being 'controversial'? Does your source have any conflicts of interest that may cause them to skew data or to lack credibility?

Avoid quoting directly from blogs, social media posts or opinion pieces as primary sources

I read blogs and social media posts, and write them too. In fact, keeping across current public discourse on your topic will necessarily involve reading them, but importantly, this is information that any person can publish without rigorous peer review. That does not make it wrong, only riskier in terms of potential errors. As primary sources, blogs and social media posts leave you open to looking (and being) uninformed. You would be wise to be wary and look elsewhere to back up your argument. The same thing is also increasingly true of opinion pieces produced by news organisations; many organisations have been cutting back on staff (including editors) for years.

When I write opinion pieces for newspapers I often provide citations but these are frequently removed to fit the style or format of the publication. It is worthwhile for me to include these citations because the editor then sees them, and I have them on hand, but the fact is that readers will often not have those citations provided for them. That means that, as a reader, you may have to look further to verify what you are reading, and as a researcher, you will always have to.

Blogs and social media posts may help back up your argument (particularly, it should be said, if your argument is about social media and blogs) but they should never be used as primary sources of information, *unless* you plan to quote from an official blog or feed of a credible organisation or individual. Even then, you should look to find better primary sources to support your argument where stats or data are concerned. The good blogs and posts will often provide citations or links to the data they are using in their arguments. Remember, there are many health blogs. There is only one World Health Organisation. Even in the event you want to argue that a major authority is wrong, you must acknowledge them and cite their data correctly. You'd best do that homework well.

If you are unsure about a blog, website or opinion piece, check for an 'About the Author' section or similar, and then look up that person elsewhere to verify whether the information posted by that author should be considered useful or accurate. If it is a social media feed, check for verification that the feed belongs to the person or organisation it claims to. Use these sources with the knowledge that they are not peer-reviewed.

Never use *Wikipedia* as a source

Wikipedia is a crowd-sourced site. That means anyone can make an entry or change the information in an entry at any time. If you take the information you find there as accurate, or cite *Wikipedia* as a source, you are taking a lot on faith and you are doing yourself and your audience a disservice. *Wikipedia* and other crowd-sourced sites may be able to provide links to credible information on a subject, but they are not themselves a credible source. Never quote *Wikipedia* (unless, of course, your subject is *Wikipedia* and the issues relating to it).

Check online information is up to date

When searching for info online, check that the article and information you find are up to date. Check the date on information or on news articles before evaluating them, and before posting or quoting them. Old articles can be very useful as long as you know that they are old. If you quote them or post them without realising they are old, you are likely to injure your argument and lose credibility.

Check the domain type in the URL

The type of website domain can provide clues as to the purpose of the site. For stats, look to credible sources like the Australian Bureau of Statistics, the World Health Organization, the World Bank and more. Be wary of advocacy or 'charity' websites that are at .com domains rather than .org, as this may indicate they are not recognised not-for-profits, even if they imply that they are. Anyone can get a .com address.

When searching for info online, look at the domain type in the URL and know what it means.

.edu – a website affiliated with a higher education institution such as a university

.gov – a federal government website

.org – an advocacy website, such as that of a not-for-profit organisation

.com – a commercial website

.net – a site from a network or internet service provider.

(Keep in mind that Australian sites will often have the suffix '.au')

Do a thorough fact check

When searching for info online, check stats, claims and quotes for accuracy. If you see a statistic or quote, there should be a link, footnote or bibliography somewhere pointing to the source of the information. Be wary of statistics that do not come with a citation. Also be sceptical of statistics that are radically out of sync with other stats used elsewhere on the topic, even if they come with a citation – being radically different *may* be an indication of selective or misleading use of data.

You can also run a simple search on information or a quote by cutting and pasting the relevant section into

Google, or whatever search engine you prefer. Where does it come up? Is this quotation used multiple times? Does it come from a credible source somewhere along the line? If it only comes up in memes or on blogs *do not use it*. Do not assume that oft-quoted statistics are correct. Make sure you see them cited by credible sources.

As mentioned earlier, check all quotes for accuracy. You should especially try not to misattribute quotes to Einstein, Gandhi, Twain – the usual suspects. Try something like quoteinvestigator.com to see if you are getting one of the common ones wrong.

Consider any copyright issues

You will also need to check on copyright issues relating to supporting quotes, images or other data or information you plan to use. Copyright laws differ from State to State and country to country, and it is your responsibility to know the relevant laws, but in general check for these things:

- Am I quoting another author or source, and if so, do I need to obtain permission? In the US short quotes, as long as they are properly attributed, are considered 'fair use'. In Australia we have 'fair dealing' laws.[6] Familiarise yourself with the standards.
- If I am using a photograph or video, do I have copyright or do I need to obtain permission to use it? If you did not take the image/video and it is not in the public domain, you will likely need permission to use it.

- Usually the best way to obtain permission is to contact the creator, though that may not always be practical or possible. The Australian Copyright Council suggests the following:

> If you want to use published material, the first point of contact is usually the publisher, who may be able to give you permission or give you some information about whom to contact. For unpublished material, the first point of contact is usually the author. Copyright Agency licenses its members' works and the works of overseas authors and publishers it represents on a pay per use basis. Copyright Agency also has available a range of other licences for associations, businesses and professionals, which are available on an annual basis. Copyright Agency can be contacted by visiting its website: www.copyright.com.au[7]

Check sources that you interview

If you are going directly to the source, rather than searching online or in existing documents, you will need to follow ethical interviewing methods, and you will also want to make sure the source is credible and reliable. Is the person directly connected with the information or telling you about it second or third hand? Are they an expert? A witness? Is there any conflict of interest? Are you able to check what they have to say, including any names, dates or other facts, against other sources?

See more on interviewing a source at:
journalistsresource.org/tip-sheets/reporting/
interviewing-a-source

And, check again

Finally, if you are basing your argument or view on a
particular fact or series of facts, or if you are directly
quoting a source, statistic or historical record when
speaking out, be sure to check it more than once, and if
possible in more than one place. Do not take information
from the first source you find without checking
elsewhere to be certain that the information is reliable.
Double- and triple-checking makes good sense, both for
your own knowledge and the knowledge that your critics
won't be able to get you on poor fact-checking.

Research your topic thoroughly and as ethically as
possible, using credible sources, and keep track of where
you get your information and data.

Knowing your stuff takes work, but it is worth it.
And keep in mind that you will likely be able to use the
information you uncover multiple times.

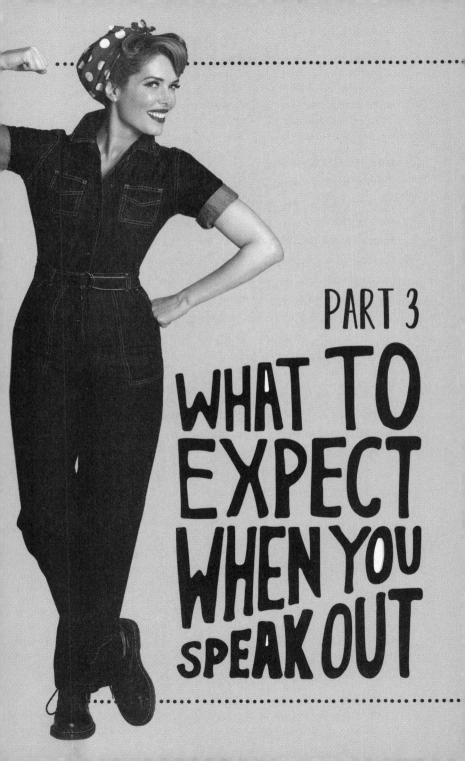

PART 3

WHAT TO EXPECT WHEN YOU SPEAK OUT

An important part of speaking out in whatever form, using whatever medium you choose, whether it is writing, public speaking, appearing on TV or organising a performance or protest, is being able to do it more than once. Applying your skills regularly allows you to hone your abilities and knowledge, become better at communicating and being heard, and can open up a career path for you, a position in leadership, a path for public advocacy or other public role for those who choose it. This allows you to take a place on a public stage which is, as we have discussed, disproportionately lacking in women's voices and influences. In other words, a public stage that needs more diversity, needs you.

Anyone speaking out will need to be prepared for what they should expect, even if they are part of that core, existing demographic of influencers. Those who are outside that core group – women, people of colour, those who are differently gendered or queer, for example – will often contend with both the usual criticism that comes with public engagement, and another level, often not so civil, aimed particularly at their difference – their female-ness, their race and so on.

The more you know about what you might expect, and what you might do about it, the better prepared you will be to keep going. In the following chapters we will tackle issues like handling criticism, recognising and responding to diversionary tactics, and surviving online spaces, as well as discussing issues like self-care, so you can speak out and keep speaking out, without burning out.

CHAPTER 7

HOW TO RECOGNISE A DIVERSION

How to spot 12 classic diversionary tactics – and not get diverted

...

Diversionary tactics are just what the term implies: tactics used to try to derail and silence an argument rather than address it. This can happen in all fields and settings, and can be particularly frustrating for women in male-dominated environments, whether in meetings or online, who find their points are ignored or not taken seriously. Some of these – like Diversions 4 and 5 listed below – may be a legitimate part of healthy debate if they are not a first response but occur as part of a more in-depth discussion, while others – like Diversions 2 and 3 – are not healthy or acceptable under any circumstances.

The individual scenarios here are used merely as descriptive examples, and each diversion could relate to many other possible topics and scenarios. Many of these examples will be familiar to readers, however, particularly those with experience on social media or in public advocacy.

Here are a dozen of the most common forms of diversionary tactic, boiled down.

Diversion 1, AKA The Faux Concern Troll

'Concern trolls' are well known online, but they exist offline as well. The faux concern is the same, regardless of the medium of communication. Any response that begins with 'Perhaps you should spend less time on X and more time on Y' should set off an alert that Diversion 1, AKA the Faux Concern Troll, may have been triggered. For example, 'Maybe you should spend less time worrying about refugees and more time worrying about poor people born in your own country.'

This is a classic, patronising response. This person feels they know more than you and they want you to know it too. They are keen to explain from

> As a rule, attacking the person instead of the argument is poor form.

their (fantasy) position of superiority that you should spend less time concerned with your issue and more time concerned about something else – usually something they find less threatening or challenging, and something that better suits their own agenda. The key here is that they do not address your points, *they immediately divert to another topic*.

This diversionary response from a Faux Concern Troll usually comes as the first response you receive from them on the topic. It often happens online or in question time after a public talk, and the person usually takes on an air of being terribly concerned for you and your misguided little ideas.

If this faux concerned critic is someone you know (or even respect), ask them why they think you are focused on the wrong issue and why another is more worthy. Often the person using this kind of diversion doesn't really give the other issue they claim is more important any credit either, they just don't want to listen to what you have to say, and they want to belittle your points or concerns. If it is a stranger who tries to derail you in this way, feel free to ignore them, as trying to get them to respectfully respond to your argument is unlikely. In an online context this can be simple – don't respond. In a public setting, like question time after a talk, you can thank the person for their view and then take a question from someone else, perhaps even saying something like 'Let's try to stay on topic'. As always, use your own judgment on whether a reply is needed, and what kind.

Obvious exceptions might include parents, loved ones, bosses, teachers and academic supervisors, who, rightly or wrongly, might have some credible or well-meaning advice about where you should be directing your energies.

Diversion 2, AKA The One Who Demeans

Rather than focusing on your argument, and acknowledging or criticising the relevant points, this person will intentionally use demeaning language to gently and (again) patronisingly suggest you are cute but dumb, nice but uneducated and so on. Attempting to demean a person instead of criticising their argument is widely recognised as poor form, bad practice and very weak. Diversion 2 often feels insulting, or like a patronising pat on the head. It resembles Diversion 3, below, but is generally subtler and less crude.

Diversion 3, AKA 'But Look at *You*'

This diversion often occurs when you are speaking out about a difficult or personal issue that has affected you and others. This critic diverts the discussion by attempting to aggressively shame you, suggesting you self-evidently deserved whatever happened to you.

Let's say you speak about your experience of discrimination, sexual assault or bullying. The Diversion 3 response might sound something like: 'No wonder. Just look at you, you ugly/fat/skinny cow/slut/etc.' Your critic doesn't like you speaking up, so they try to belittle your appearance, size, weight, alleged sexual history and so on.

> Let's be clear: assault, bullying and discrimination are never the fault of the person who is being discriminated against and no one deserves to be spoken to in this manner.

As a rule, attacking the person instead of the argument is poor form. This is an aggressive style of diversion and silencing, even more demeaning than Diversion 2, and is often outright bullying. It's a classic scenario and generally the easiest diversion to spot because it is so openly hostile, and often crude. But it can also be difficult if it triggers a certain emotional response in you, and this is often the malicious aim.

Let's be clear: assault, bullying and discrimination are never the fault of the person who is being discriminated against and no one deserves to be spoken to in this manner. Try not to let it get to you. Those who use this tactic are simply not worth it.

If you find that individuals like this are getting to you, remember that you deserve better, reach out to a trusted friend, and don't forget to look after yourself. (Read the section on **self-care** in this book for more information, page 259.) Your response to such an attack (if you feel you need to make one) can be as simple as 'I won't dignify such a low remark with a response' or simply '*That* is your argument?'

Diversion 4, AKA 'But What About the Middle East?'

Say you present information on violent attacks against LGBTIQ people in your community. One diversionary response is: 'You think gays have it bad here? *What about in the Middle East?*'

> Don't stop talking about and circulating credible information on important issues. Awareness isn't everything, but it matters, and can make a real difference in bringing about action and change.

This tactic is frequently used to divert discussions about various freedoms, or social or safety issues impacting women, children, LGBTIQ people, sex workers, people with a disability, racial minorities and so on. The basic argument is that nothing needs to be done at home because things are worse elsewhere. People are being bashed? Well they are being murdered somewhere else. Women are raped and murdered here? It's worse somewhere else. It aims to shut down an uncomfortable topic by pointing the finger elsewhere, to another country or culture, or even to a former time when things were harder. This does nothing to solve the issue at hand, and serves only to push away any sense of there being a real and immediate problem.

Don't be diverted. Problems at home, and in the here and now, matter too.

Diversion 5, AKA Textbook Diversion, or 'What About Men?'

This is a textbook first-reply diversion (along the lines of Diversion 4), in which the responder attempts to change the subject immediately. For example, let's say you talk about reports of high rates of domestic abuse against a particular demographic: women. The diversionary response is: 'What about men?' It's not that this question should not be raised – it should. Rather, this question demands immediate discussion of a different topic, which is what makes it a textbook diversion.

This tactic is frequently used to divert discussions of gendered patterns in violence, as many feminists and advocates are well aware. It is true that some men experience terrible domestic violence and some women are perpetrators. It is true that men are also attacked and killed in our society, and with more frequency than women. However, statistically the murders of men are largely by other adult men *outside* the home, and the murders of women are largely by adult men *inside* the home. Women, when they are murdered, are most commonly killed by a former or current intimate partner (a staggering 70% of the time), and one woman is killed by a current or former partner in Australia on average once or twice a week every week, so the issue of violence against women in the home is a significant one with a large death toll. Women kill their current or former partners too, but that is considerably rarer. The fact that anyone with an intimate partner can be the victim of domestic violence does not mean that the strikingly gendered patterns of domestic violence should be ignored. In fact, without analysing the existing patterns, we can't put in place a response, let alone solutions. This is particularly important as gender inequality has now been widely recognised as a root cause of violence against women,[1] worldwide.

Diversion 5 often comes with an addition along the lines of 'All violence is bad'. This is absolutely true. But specificity is also important. Talking about one thing does not mean you don't care about something else. Diverting the topic to another – in this case far less demographically common – issue is a classic diversionary tactic, and in some cases an attempt to neutralise the argument.

Diversion 6, AKA 'DO Something About It'

You publish a post on social media about a particular issue – let's say about reports on how underage refugees are locked in detention centres, causing concern by major welfare bodies and the United Nations, or how appalling it is that a particular species is dying out due to climate change. The diversionary response is: 'If you care so much, DO something about it; otherwise shut up.'

It does not logically follow that social media posts are useless. Raising awareness is the essence of any statement or report by whistleblowers or war correspondents. We wouldn't respond to these worthy reports by saying 'Do something about it'. Further, posting on social media does not preclude the possibility of taking other action. In fact, those who are actively employed in 'doing something' on the ground about issues frequently welcome discussion that raises awareness, and actively employ social media to help bring issues to the attention of the public. In my work for UNICEF, for example, social media is often employed in important fundraising, or to raise awareness about an issue and lobby the government for change.

In short, it is very unlikely that your critic is one of those doers. He or she is more likely not doing anything about it and

Do your thing ... If yours is a good cause and you can do something, do it. Do not be diverted from that.

simply doesn't want you talking about it because it makes him or her uncomfortable.

Don't stop talking about and circulating credible information on important issues. Awareness isn't everything, but it matters, and can make a real difference in bringing about action and change.

Diversion 7, AKA 'If You Can't Do Everything, Do Nothing'

Let's say you are raising money for a charity appeal that helps get basic toiletry supplies to people experiencing homelessness. The diversionary response is: 'If you really cared about homelessness you would be opening your home to them.'

This argument boils down to: 'If you can't do everything, you can't do anything, therefore no one should do anything.' My guess is this critic is doing just that: precisely nothing.

Do your thing. No one can champion all causes, or do everything at once for every person. Anyone can try to divert you by pointing to a more extreme example, but it takes real heart to do anything at all. Change comes about through actions both large and small. If yours is a good cause and you can do something, do it. Modest fundraising is still fundraising. Volunteering for one cause doesn't change everything wrong with the world but it still makes a difference. Do not be diverted from that.

Too many people do nothing – or worse, try to stop others from doing anything. Don't let them stop you.

Diversion 8, AKA 'I Challenge You to Explain Everything'

Let's say you point out the well-documented gender pay gap. The usual diversionary response is: 'There are laws against unequal pay. I challenge you to provide one example of an instance where a man has been paid more than a woman for the same job.'

The reason why this is a diversion is that the gender pay gap is something that has been exhaustively documented for decades. It's like reporting that a building has collapsed, and instead of being able to focus on those who have been disadvantaged by this disaster, or how it happened and might be prevented in future, you are being challenged to prove gravity exists.

Further, just because something is outlawed does not mean it doesn't happen. It is against the law to murder people and yet people get murdered every week. If your critic 'challenges' you to explain something that is already well known, it is most likely a diversion.

My usual response to Diversion 8 is to have the names of a few credible, impartial organisations up my sleeve (the Australian Bureau of Statistics, World Health Organisation, Human Rights Commission, etc) and to ask the person to go ahead and research it for themselves. Many issues, like the pay gap, are complex and require time to research properly. There are a lot of factors involved. It's not your job to do that work for them.

If they do challenge you in this way, it's possible they genuinely want to learn more about the issue. Often, however, their challenge is an attempt to draw focus towards themselves instead of the issue, or to claim the issue is imagined because you refuse to waste your time explaining this already well-documented thing to them.

Diversion 9, AKA 'Who Do You Think You Are?'/'Shame On You!'/'How Dare You!'

Like many classic diversions, this one is intended to completely shut down debate. Let's say you have some concerns about a law or public policy. The diversionary response might be something like: 'You think you know better than the government?' or 'Laws are laws for a reason.' The person has not addressed your points, whatever those are. Basically they are saying: 'How dare you question the omnipotent and perfect functioning of our impartial and flawless parliamentary or judicial systems?'

Well, look, if such systems were perfect and impartial, slavery would not have been legal and it wouldn't have taken the Civil War to change that in the US. This kind of response might also trigger accusations of 'Shame on you' for bringing up a particular subject. It's a whole lot of 'Who do you think you are?', because apparently having opinions is for other people, not you.

Democracy involves public debate. As long as it is done respectfully, debate is a very good and very important thing. We need people to question the status quo. Without them, we'd probably still be stoning adulterers and keeping slaves.

Diversion 10, AKA The Semantic Loop, or 'Not All Men'

Let's take two completely random headlines using the word 'men' or 'women':

- **'Acadiana barista helps men discover inner strength',** *The Advertiser.*[2] The article reads: 'Dallas Begnaud is a spiritual guide and storyteller with The Inner Kingdom. He works with men to develop internal strengths in a world that can demand so much.'
- **'American women increasingly interested in terrorism',** *CBS News.*[3] The article states: 'It's unusual for a woman to be involved in mass violence in the United States. But the increasing number of women drawn to ISIS is worrisome to American law enforcement and making it almost impossible to flag the prototypical recruit for investigation.'

These headlines are reasonably straightforward. From these, we would be unlikely to infer that *all* men are helped by a barista/want to discover inner strength, or *all* American women are interested in terrorism. The reason we are unlikely to infer these things is that each of them would be a) impossible and b) absurd. In either case, we can infer through common sense and common use of language that a particular subset of people is being referred to – men who spend time with a particular barista, or some American females interested in terrorism.

For this reason, it is very curious that people (almost invariably men, sadly) can be found across the web, insisting that they have been wronged by women who use common phrases like 'I hate it when men catcall me', or 'We need to address male violence'. Very few people would take such statements as affronts to them personally, because they are clearly not being referred to. It's men who catcall who are being pointed out. Or it's men who are violent.

Put simply, this semantic argument isn't debate, it isn't pointing out the nuanced issues relating to violence and gender, it is a ploy to shut things down or shift the focus somewhere else. (Likewise '#notallwhites' and other responses to discussions of large patterns of behaviour, crime etc.) In the words of feminist writer Bailey Poland,

> No amount of "some" will ever be enough to stave them off … It is important to understand that "not all men" men are not the product of failed grammar lessons. Their reading of any use of the word "men" as implicitly incriminating "all men" is a deliberate rhetorical strategy employed for the purposes of disrupting a conversation and attempting to undermine an observation. The strategy is an attempt to stop women from making change or having productive discussions by keeping the speaker mired in semantic arguments about her word choice.[4]

When this ploy is used – particularly against women and girls speaking out about painful and traumatic experiences of violence, rape or intimidation – it's worth pausing and considering what kind of person thinks it is OK to undermine a woman's right to speak out about trauma with a semantic argument that is rarely if ever applied to any other subject? The answer: probably not the kind of person you should feel the need to try to appease.

Diversion 11, AKA The Old Switcheroo

This is an aggressive style of diversion that often aims to both silence and insult. Whatever point you have brought up regarding a particular problem, this person will suggest or strongly claim that *you* are an example of precisely that problem, but the thing you pointed out is *not*. Mention an instance of sexism and this person will instantly accuse you of being sexist. Raise the issue of racism, and they will call you racist. Highlight some example of bullying and you are 'the real bully'. Express concern about low wages for the working majority and you are accused of waging 'class warfare'. Black is white, up is down, and nowhere does this actually make sense.

Plainly, the act of pointing out, advocating against or keeping data on gender-based discrimination is not sexist, and focusing on an issue regarding race or racism is not racist. Responding with a claim that it is not only suggests a lack of logic and a deep misunderstanding of the issues, but also reveals a desire to shut down any conversation about those issues.

This is one of the oldest, laziest styles of 'debate' going, an unnecessary form of name-calling that sadly has been used to some effect in public spin campaigns to distract or neutralise legitimate debate about issues.

Diversion 12: A Textbook Sampling of the Above

It's common enough for a person seeking to divert or shut down debate to pepper their response with a sampling of the above techniques. They rarely hit 11 out of 11, but if they do, give them a special prize for it, because that is truly impressive.

Here is a real-life example of a response to a post I wrote,

> Democracy involves public debate. As long as it is done respectfully, debate is a very good and very important thing.

linking to a SBS news article[5] regarding the racist taunts received by legendary Sydney Swans football player, former Australian of the Year and proud Indigenous man Adam Goodes:

> Cute and uneducated opinion Tara moss. Look back over 15 years of support for Adam. And see it lost when he chose to defy the gentleman's code of the game. great to see you are no better than a racist!! stereotyping everyone over a common action rather than treating each individual as an individual. Shame on you …

Now leaving aside that I didn't write the piece I was linking to, you can see that he ticked the boxes for Diversion 2 ('Cute and uneducated'), Diversion 11 ('you are no better than a racist!!'), and Diversion 9 ('Shame on you').

Ticking three out of eleven boxes in one first response to a discussion is a classic Number 12.

In public life, or when speaking out in any context, you are likely to encounter diversionary tactics. Know that this is common and that it is not a reflection on you or your argument. Stand your ground, speak out, and do not be diverted.

Bingo!

There are some helpful versions of Bingo! out there, where you can see just how many boxes your critic or troll ticks off. When it comes to women who speak out against sexual harassment, inequality and related matters, the Bingo! boxes commonly contain things like 'fat', 'ugly', 'irrational', 'needs to get laid', 'imagining things' (see **Gaslighting** on pages 151 to 154), 'hormonal', humourless', 'hysterical' and 'shrill'. Horrible, all, but the fact that so many critics still fall back on these responses when communicating with women is telling. Bingo games highlight just how commonly these slurs are used in response to women who speak out. In short, these responses are *not* about you.

Here is a version of Antifeminist Gaslighting Bingo created by Sarah Grey (@GreyEditing), again highlighting the lack of originality of certain types of critics. Grey tweeted this August 2015 as an aid to Megyn Kelly, the Fox journalist harassed by presidential hopeful Donald Trump and his supporters for daring to confront him and his many questionable comments on women. You could practically tick each one off, reading the hate directed at her online. (In addition to publicly calling her 'crazy',[6] Trump referred to her as a 'bimbo',[7] too, so that's another one to add to the playlist. I've copped that plenty of times.)

Antifeminist Gaslighting Bingo				
Fat/Ugly	Irrational	Fascist	Prude	Imagining things
Self-aggrandizing	Needs to get laid	SJW (Social Justice Warrior)	Feminazi	Hates free speech
Hormonal	Crazy	**Why are you so angry, we gave you this Free Space**	PC police	Needs to get a life
Biased	Humorless	Bitch	Overly emotional	Can't take a joke
Controlling	Hysterical	Misandrist	Shrill	Looking for reasons to be offended

There are loads more. See:

- Anti-feminist comic bingo: ireadcomics.blogspot.com/2007/04/anti-comics-feminist-bingo.html
- Feminist conference speaker bingo ('The next time you're advocating to have a woman-identified person keynote a conference, why not make convincing your colleagues into a fun game!'): www.ijfab.org/blog/feminist-conference-speaker-bingo/
- Anti-feminist gaslighting bingo: twitter.com/Lyndsay_Kirkham/status/627502410454421504
- Street Harassment Bingo/Street Harassment Misogynoir: twitter.com/thetrudz/status/486593280897863680?ref_src=twsrc%5Etfw

CHAPTER 8

HANDLING CRITICISM

Tips for surviving criticism

...

When you speak out, you will have critics. I cannot write this book and pretend that you won't. Though it may not always feel good, criticism is a good sign, a solid indication that you are being heard – or possibly misheard. Criticism is a great teacher, and for me, often an energiser as well. It is possible not only to survive criticism, but also to emerge the better for it, whether that criticism is nasty or constructive. (If you're going to speak out online, you'll also want to take a good look at **Chapters 11** and **12**, which deal with a lot of criticisms specific to digital platforms such as social media.)

When you speak out you will inevitably voice arguments that some will disagree with. Some people will not like your presentation style, your voice or writing, your topic or your perspective. Others may be great supporters, but will still take issue with some of your specific points. You may even find that there are those who don't like *you*, and for some reason really want you to know it. Whatever the situation, you will find yourself needing to deal with criticism at some point. The most renowned and influential thinkers, speakers and activists in the world cop regular criticism, and it has ever been thus.

> Though it may not always feel good, criticism is a good sign, a solid indication that you are being heard - or possibly misheard.

If you are criticised, know that it is not automatically an indication of failure, even if it is sometimes a sign that improvements are needed. In fact, if you don't get *any* criticism it may be a sure sign that you aren't reaching a wide enough audience, and certainly not challenging the status quo. Not all criticism is equal, but handling any kind of criticism well is a great skill to have, and a rare one.

Here are some things we can all do to improve our ability to survive criticism:

1. Be prepared

Know that you will be criticised, and be mentally prepared for it. Importantly, when you speak out your arguments should also be prepared thoroughly enough for you to be able to withstand criticism. (See **Chapter 6: Knowing Your Stuff**.) If you go in knowing that you are on solid ground with your argument, criticism will be less likely, less total, and will probably hurt you far less. If you have prepared well, ideally you will even expect a lot of the specific critiques you end up receiving. If you receive criticism you *weren't* expecting, try to look at it objectively to see if there is truth in what is being said, and whether it's something you can learn from. Preparation will help to avoid these issues, but realistically, it can't guarantee that you'll receive no valid criticism. Even the best prepared speaker, writer or commentator will make mistakes, overlook important points or be misinterpreted.

2. Know that criticism is not failure, and failure is not the end

Criticism and failure are two things that most successful people experience a lot. Those who put themselves under pressure to try new things, to create or develop projects or businesses, or test out new skills or ideas, tend to fail more often than those who stick to the same things throughout their lives. Almost everyone experiences criticism at some stage. But let me be clear: *criticism is not failure*, even if it is failure to please one particular critic, at one particular point in time.

Many people have been criticised in ways that could have been interpreted as an

If you are criticised, know that it is not automatically an indication of failure, even if it is sometimes a sign that improvements are needed.

irreversible failure, only to go on to become one of the finest in their field. Think of Oprah Winfrey, who was fired as a reporter because she was supposedly 'unfit for TV', or Lucille Ball, who was repeatedly sent home from acting school for having 'no talent'.[1] On one school report, the brilliant novelist Charlotte Brontë copped this: 'She writes indifferently … and knows nothing of grammar, geography, history or accomplishments.'[2] Thomas Edison, who patented the first commercially successful lightbulb in 1879, was told in his early years that he was 'too stupid to learn anything', and ground-breaking scientist Charles Darwin wrote of his childhood, 'I was considered by all my masters and my father, a very ordinary boy, rather below the common standard of intellect.'[3]

In short, critics are not always right.

Some people rise up despite heavy criticism from an early age. Pamela Young – an Indigenous actor and one of the Stolen Generation – was brought up in foster care and says she learned 'to be ashamed of who you are, you are the lowest denominator in race, so you will achieve nothing when you grow up, you'll be a servant to people'.[4] She has since had success in many fields, appearing in film and TV both nationally and internationally.

Others are simply underestimated or misunderstood. In my youth I was often told that I was 'the pretty one' and my sister was 'the smart one', as if the two things were somehow mutually exclusive. Naturally, after a while this notion sank in, becoming part of my own narrative, but after a career as a model in my teens and early twenties I realised that writing was where my passion really was. I went on to write 10 books (this is my 11th), become a doctoral student at the University of Sydney, and pursue academic life and life as a public speaker and advocate. My public career has involved plenty of criticism and failure, but praise and success as well.

Criticism is not the end. Particularly if you handle it well, learn from it, or see it as a call to arms.

Identifying constructive criticism

Now for the good stuff.

As I've mentioned, not all criticism is equal. While it may be tempting to see all criticism of you or your work as objectionable or ill-founded, constructive criticism is in fact the opposite, potentially pointing you towards a greater understanding of your chosen topic. Criticism of this kind is a vital part of the process of communication, debate and learning. It has great value.

Depending on the situation, the source of the criticism and your personality or state of mind, it can sometimes be challenging to spot good criticism and separate it from the bad. Although it is not so easy to break down what is constructive and what is not – it will depend on the context and topic – here are four simple steps for identifying constructive criticism.

Step 1: Does the criticism address your specific argument?

If the criticism is a diversion (see the previous chapter) or completely peripheral to your argument, then the answer is 'No'. If the answer is 'Yes, it does address my specific argument', proceed to the next step.

Step 2: Does the source have credibility?

Who is criticising you or your work? If it is someone you respect, or who has authority in your workplace, institution or field, you will obviously want to take heed. It does not mean they are necessarily right, but it does mean they are likely to have a good point and that their criticism will need addressing. The wisest thing is to listen and take it on board.

If the criticism is not from someone you know, someone you respect, or someone who is an authority in the area you are speaking or writing on, you may wish to:

- consider whether, on the face of it, the criticism has merit and should be investigated further, or has no merit and should be ignored entirely
- look to see if it fits within a larger pattern of criticism you are receiving (see Step 3)
- check to see if the source is known for this kind of criticism.

Unfortunately, there are plenty of people in the public eye or online who have a track record of publicly vilifying high-profile women, those who are LGBTIQ, or those who speak out about inequality, sexism, racism, homophobia, ableism (discrimination against those with a disability) or other issues. Look up the profile of the person who is criticising you to see if they are notorious for being one of those individuals. If it is clear that the criticism is coming from a place of bigotry, sexism, resentment or trolling that is unrelated to your real argument, work or abilities, you may wish to take steps to avoid that person in the future. On social media, you can ban or block (see **Chapters 11** and **12**), while in the physical world it may be less easy.

If a person who is notorious for racism, bigotry, sexism or generally being offensive has had a go at you, break out the champagne. You are almost certainly doing something right. If someone I don't respect writes something negative about me, I consider it a good review.

Step 3: Do you sense they may have a valid point in their criticism?

This is a tricky one. Your 'sense' in this respect may be incorrect, and sometimes accurate criticism can be something you initially feel upset by. In some cases, however, criticism of an argument will catch your attention precisely because it gives you a hunch that the person criticising you may be right, or at least partially right. If that happens, go with that instinct, at least until you can analyse the feeling, and can decide to your own satisfaction whether that criticism has merit or not. If your instinct is that yes, the criticism may have value, you may want to look at Step 4.

Step 4: Are there any patterns to the criticism you are receiving?

Have you heard this criticism before or seen it levelled at others? Have *you* perhaps levelled it at others? If you find you are getting a lot of criticism about the same issues, this may be a good indication that these critics have a valid point or points to offer you. It could help you to understand your topic better and lessen the potential for making similar mistakes in the future.

Alternatively, it may be that you are experiencing a kind of criticism that you already know your position on. The criticism may simply indicate that you are dealing with a large or vocal group that disagrees with your views. Finding patterns of criticism can be very helpful.

If the pattern of criticism indicates that more research or self-reflection is required, thank your critic, and tell them you will take on board what they have told you. You could ask them for more information, including citations or links and suggestions for further reading. This is where you can most benefit from your critics.

It could be that you have overlooked an important aspect of your topic. No one is perfect. When you do your research you may find that this is a common issue in your field or on the topic. One example is a criticism of your work as exclusionary or biased. If you get this criticism and give it some consideration, you may see how you *did* unintentionally exclude certain groups or show some unconscious bias, and how you could correct that in the future. (An apology could be in order – see **Making public apologies** on pages 154 to 155.)

Even if you look into the issues your critics raise and find that you still disagree or feel they are in error, you will have a deeper understanding of the issues involved and you may be more prepared for similar criticism down the track.

If the pattern of criticism indicates that you are dealing with a group of people who oppose your views but do not have any constructive criticisms to point out to you – which is common in disagreements about

politics, feminism and more – you can take the feedback
on board as an indication of what you are up against.
This kind of criticism frequently energises me, even as it
frustrates me.

Step 5: Take it on board

Once you have established that the criticism is aimed
at your specific argument, the source has credibility,
you sense that the person or people may have a point
or it is part of a meaningful pattern, you are on track
to considering whether this criticism has merit, and
whether you can learn from it when you speak out in the
future.

What to do when you are criticised
...

What should you do when you are criticised? Take time to absorb what is happening, and try to remain objective. Before responding, consider what the issues are and the source of the criticism, and then consider what this criticism tells you.

Step 1: Take a moment

Try not to respond immediately. Sometimes a few seconds is all it takes to ascertain why you have been

> Know that you will be criticised, and be mentally prepared for it.

criticised and to figure out the best response. Sometimes it will take much longer, particularly if the criticism is upsetting or unexpected. Give yourself the time you need to respond properly, or to make a decision not to respond at all. This is a learned habit, and tends to become easier with experience.

Step 2: Find out what the specific issues are

Some criticism is not very specific. For instance, if you have filed a report or written a blog and someone you work with or respect writes 'Redo this', ask that person as calmly as possibly to explain precisely what the problems are: 'Can you be more specific?' or 'Can you tell me what you don't like about it?' This can spark helpful conversations. (Obviously if the criticism is a trolling comment from a stranger, feel free to ignore it.)

According to productivity training consultant Garrett Miller, 'What' questions, such as 'What evidence did you see?', tend to draw out more helpful information than those that begin with 'Why?', such as 'Why are you saying that?', which can produce resentment.[5]

However, I find 'Why?' questions are very helpful in interview situations. Decide for yourself what the best approach is, depending on who is criticising you and why.

Step 3: Identify whether the criticism is constructive
(See **Identifying constructive criticism** on pages 143 to 147.)

Step 4: Avoid interpreting critiques of your work as personal criticisms of you
Sometimes, when criticism is not kind, catches you on a bad day, or shakes your self-esteem or sense of identity, it can be easy to see the criticism as a devastating critique of you as a person. Try to look at what is being criticised and what is not. Is the criticism about you? If not, don't make it about you, make it about your work. If the criticism *is* about you, again, consider the source. Why are *you* being criticised? Often those who aim their criticism at people rather than ideas do not have much to offer in the way of constructive feedback.

Step 5: Are you offending people?
And finally, if a lot of people express offence at your statements, consider why that might be, and whether an apology is in order. We all make mistakes. Recognising them can be quite useful, and public apologies, when done right, can be powerful. (See **Making public apologies** on pages 154 to 155.)

On the other hand, people are offended by a range of different things that can't always be predicted, and it could be that you are challenging the status quo, which is going to lead to complaints from some people with different ideas to yours. Try to be open-minded and consider what might be going on before deciding to respond.

Remember, criticism is vital

...

While no one likes being criticised, and some criticism can really hurt, criticism is inevitable and can be positive. It can be constructive and help you expand your knowledge, consider another view or realise you've made false assumptions, or (ironically) it can be so poor or biased that it further confirms your own argument. Whatever the criticism tells you – whether it speaks to a flaw in your work or simply shows that you are 'poking in the right fireplace' – it is important to handle it as well as possible, and that means separating the constructive critics from the unconstructive trolls, and deciding how to respond, if at all.

> Not all criticism is equal, but handling any kind of criticism well is a great skill to have, and a rare one.

Remember, criticism is vital. Without critical feedback, your work suffers. Sometimes it can be the best thing for you. It can even help inspire and fuel your work. It certainly helps mine.

It is not easy to be on the receiving end of criticism. It is true that not all criticism is equal – some will be constructive and some will not – but handling criticism well is a great skill to have, and one worth cultivating.

Gaslighting

Sometimes, in your public or private life, you may find yourself subject to something called 'gaslighting'. This phenomenon goes well beyond normal criticism, and is a form of manipulation and in more serious cases, mental abuse, that all women and girls should be aware of.

In a nutshell, gaslighting involves using false information with the intention of disorienting the target and making them doubt their own memory, knowledge and sanity – usually to further the opponent's or abuser's own agenda. Gaslighting can be particularly relevant for women and for those speaking out about abuse or injustice on behalf of either themselves or others. It may occur in a public debate, online, in the workplace, classroom or in private situations.

Why 'gaslighting'?

The term comes from the 1938 Patrick Hamilton play *Gas Light* (also known as *Angel Street*) about a woman whose husband manipulates her slowly but surely into believing she is insane. This essentially gets her out of the way, while he searches for the missing jewels of a woman in the attic upstairs, whom he has murdered. In addition to isolating his new wife by cutting her off from friends and other points of view (another common tactic to beware of), he makes subtle, unexplained changes to her environment, convincing her she is misplacing things and imagining things. When he is in the attic, using gaslight to explore the woman's possessions, the lights in the rest of the house dim; his wife naturally notices this, but he tells her it is in her head. The play was adapted into a 1940 British film and a famous 1944 American film, starring Ingrid Bergman and Charles Boyer. In her book *Damaged Identities, Narrative Repair*, Hilde Lindemann Nelson writes of the 1944 film:

> [If] Boyer is given sufficient time to destroy Bergman's sense of self-worth altogether, and if her loving trust in him causes her to accept his verdict regarding her mental state as definitive, then Bergman will not be able to rely on her judgments, no matter how much evidence presents itself regarding her husband's deception.[6]

This chillingly describes the effects of gaslighting. It is now recognised as a psychological method of abuse used by bullies, trolls, victim-blamers, child abusers, and intimate partners in the context of domestic abuse or violence. It can come in the form of simple, one-off statements or acts of manipulation and denial, or in more sophisticated, ongoing forms, particularly in cases of domestic or family abuse. Ultimately, the victim of gaslighting is encouraged to believe they don't really know what they know, and can't be sure of what they think or feel.

While gaslighting can have particularly devastating effects in the context of domestic abuse, as in the

Patrick Hamilton play mentioned above, it also applies to bullying tactics in public debate, in the workplace, and online. The historical tendency for women to be cast as illogical, hysterical and unreliable witnesses to their own lives and experiences, makes gaslighting a technique that women in particular should watch out for.

Are you experiencing gaslighting?

Gaslighting can be subtle, and can sometimes take place over long periods, making it difficult to spot. Here are 10 signs that you may be experiencing gaslighting, privately or publicly:

1. You are told you are being emotional, hysterical or crazy, and that you don't know what you are talking about.
2. You find yourself frequently apologising.
3. You are told you 'deserved' or 'asked for' something bad that happened to you, including assault, abuse or harassment.
4. Your self-esteem or trust in your own judgment is low.
5. You feel you 'don't know your own mind', frequently second-guess yourself and have difficulty making decisions.
6. These days you often feel confused, and you don't trust your memories or perceptions.
7. You can't understand why you are not happy, with so many apparently 'good things' in your life.

8. You find yourself withholding information from colleagues, friends, family or authorities so you don't have to explain or make excuses about your actions or the actions of your partner, colleague or boss.
9. You sense something is wrong, but you can't quite express what it is, even to yourself.
10. You feel depressed, anxious, 'crazy' or fearful. You also feel that you used to be more confident, more relaxed and with more of a social life.

Remember, *gaslighting is not regular criticism*, it is manipulation. Check for the signs in both your private and public interactions and relationships, and most importantly of all, look after yourself (see **Chapter 15: Self-care**).

Making public apologies

...

Making a public apology is never easy, but it can be incredibly powerful. We all make mistakes, and if you have been shown to have made a mistake, the best thing you can do is own up to it. This is your opportunity to show the rare skill of handling criticism positively.

Remember:

This too will pass.

Don't get angry.

Don't deny it.

Don't blame others.

We all make mistakes, and if you have been shown to have made a mistake, the best thing you can do is own up to it.

Blueprint for an apology

If your mistake was public, your apology will likely need to be public. If you do need to apologise publicly, do it with as much grace as possible. Here are some tips you will want to keep in mind:

- Be unreserved in your apology
- Avoid making excuses for your mistake
- Take responsibility. Own your mistake.

If you are going to apologise, do it. Be sure to use the words 'I am sorry' or 'I apologise'.

Consider using the same medium to speak your apology as you did to speak your mistake. If it was in person, try to apologise in person. If it was on a social media platform, use the same social media platform. Consider what medium would be most appropriate without causing further offense or inconvenience to those who have been slighted.

Say sorry and say it simply. Don't embellish that 'sorry' with words that detract from it. For instance, 'I'm sorry if I caused offence' is not a great apology. People who use qualifications like 'if' often seem sorrier that they got in trouble than they are for what they said or did. If you are at the stage of publicly apologising for causing offence or harm, there is no 'if' about it. Apologise unreservedly. Don't add any 'ifs'. When you are wrong, saying 'I was wrong, and I am sorry' can potentially alleviate some of the grief felt by those you have hurt or offended, raise your esteem in the eyes of others and open up new positive opportunities.

CHAPTER 9

KNOWING HOW AND WHEN TO SAY NO

Saying no to invitations to speak out

...

In your career or not-for-profit advocacy, perhaps as a direct result of speaking out, you may be asked to give presentations, lectures or talks, participate in festivals, panels or radio or television programs, or write opinion pieces or guest blogs, among other things. If this happens it is excellent news, but now you need to decide whether this opportunity is right for you.

> Just because you have agreed to be there, does not mean you have agreed to answer anything that is asked.

What is the reputation of the event, publication, program or organisers?

Always do some research into what you are being asked to do, and by whom, before you agree. If you need to, stall by saying you have to check your calendar. (Most people have time pressures and schedules to juggle, so this is a legitimate response. I genuinely have to check my calendar regularly, as I negotiate full-time work, writing, being a uni student and being a mum.)

If it is an interview, who will be interviewing you? What kind of questions might you expect? What kind of publication will it appear in?

If you are being asked to write, look at other articles, blogs or books by the same publisher. What is the tone of the publication you'll be contributing to? Are there any conflicts of interest?

If it is a panel, conference, festival or radio or TV program, who are the other guests?

If possible, always view or listen to a sample broadcast before appearing on any radio or TV show. It may only take you 15 minutes, but it will be time very well spent, as it can give you clues as to the format, tone and political bent of the show, and what to expect.

Will you be paid?

If the opportunity is freelance or not already part of your existing work arrangements, find out if you will be paid, and if not, why not? Is it for a charity? Is it part of an internship? Don't be afraid to ask.

When being asked to speak, there is a big difference between festivals and corporate events, and a big difference between interviews, panels, keynote speaker and moderator or emcee roles, both in terms of the work, preparation involved and professional expectations, so be sure to find out more about what is expected of you and what compensation is appropriate. For example, TV and radio programs that interview guests rarely pay those guests. If you are asked to host a show, yes; if you are asked on as a guest to talk about your project, no. Likewise, if you are asked for a quote for a newspaper article, then no, it is not a professional engagement so there is no pay; if you are asked to write a newspaper article, yes, it is a professional engagement and you should be paid. Festivals and some community events generally pay modest fees or offer an 'honorary fee' so participants will not be out of pocket, while keynote speakers will sometimes get paid quite a bit more, depending on the context, the speaker and the preparation involved. Find out what is standard in your particular field.

> If the opportunity is freelance or not already part of your existing work arrangements, find out if you will be paid, and if not, why not? Don't be afraid to ask.

Sometimes when I'm asked to appear at community or charity events, art projects and so on, I will ask for fuel money and other expenses, and this works well for the organisers even though there is a minimal budget for the event. This has helped me get by on many occasions, so don't be afraid to ask. Other times I am asked to speak at a 'charity event' only to find that it is a paid event with high ticket prices and high profits. But because there is an auction or other charity component, the organisers try to get performers or speakers for free by passing the event off as 'for charity'. Look out for this. I've fallen for it.

It is worth asking if others are being paid in these situations. I have learned a great deal through speaking to agents who have tipped me off that the organisers of the speaking event I am being asked to participate in as a freebie routinely pay large sums to other speakers and performers. I find this sort of approach unethical, as I believe it is better to be upfront about the nature of the event, rather than only paying those who speak out and push for more information. If you are the only person on a panel who isn't being paid, it isn't good for your wallet or your reputation.

Get into the habit of asking about fees as a routine part of your professional exchanges. A basic blueprint would be something like: 'Thank you for this opportunity. I'll see if that date is available in my calendar. What is your budget for speakers/writers/participants?' If it feels from the start as if it may not be a paying job, you may prefer to ask 'Is there a budget?' rather than 'What is your budget?'

If you are speaking out as a writer, most publications and some blogs have a standard rate per word to offer for original work or a rate they can offer for republishing blog posts from your site. Paid writing may come with a contract asking for exclusive rights to publish etc. Look over any contracts carefully, and know that many can be negotiated and changed on request. I have often changed the terms of standard contracts when faced with outrageous clauses about the right to use my words, anywhere in the world, sold on to any third party, in perpetuity, without further permissions, payments etc, all for a paltry sum. If anything concerns you, get legal advice.

> Look over any contracts carefully, and know that many can be negotiated and changed on request.

Alternatively, you may cross out the section you don't agree with, re-write it and let the publication know you would like those terms changed. Do this *before* you sign.

> Not being paid or being underpaid is statistically more likely to happen to women than men - partly because women are less likely to talk about money and negotiate fees.

You may also be asked to provide comments for free by journalists, academics or others. This is usually done over the phone or by email, or in the studio for TV or radio interviews. (I personally prefer to *write* my answers to journalist's questions if the piece is to appear only in print, because although this takes longer, I am a writer and I prefer to write the words of mine that will be read as quotes in text. It is my preference to reply in the medium in which I will be read or heard, though this doesn't work for everyone.) This sort of thing is not a professional engagement and is not paid.

If you have ideas you want to share, you may want to say yes to a certain amount of media exposure, or to being included in other writing projects such as books, blogs or academic articles, which can obviously be of benefit. Remember, however, that you don't need to say yes to every request and that the time you commit to unpaid comment can't be endless. As always, decide for yourself.

Whatever the opportunity, if the people involved decline to offer any payment, consider whether you still want to participate. If they aren't offering enough, consider negotiating. If this feels uncomfortable at first, or if you have a bad first experience with it, make sure you persist. This is what professionals do, and it is expected.

Not being paid or being underpaid is statistically more likely to happen to women than men – partly because women are less likely to talk about money and negotiate fees. Remember, you deserve to be compensated for your time, effort, expertise and skills.

Work vs exposure

In the early days you may be more inclined to say yes, even to unpaid professional opportunities, because you will benefit in other ways, like gaining experience, contacts and exposure. This is a good instinct, but regardless, you'll want to find out about the event, program or publication and its reputation beforehand, and you will also want to ask whether others are being paid. Always consider what is right for you, and don't allow yourself to feel pressured to say yes just because someone else thinks it is an 'opportunity' for you.

Hesitating?

If it looks like a good opportunity but you feel anxious about participating, try to work out why. Sometimes you'll feel reluctant to push yourself out of your comfort zone and speak out to a large audience. Sometimes you are simply too busy to fit more into your schedule. Other times it may be that something about the event or opportunity doesn't seem right.

> The point is, you are a human being, you have rights, and you don't have to answer anything you don't want to.

If you don't feel comfortable with the publication, program or event, or the people behind it, don't participate. You can decide whether you want to tell them why, or whether you want to take the sometimes easier route of simply being 'unavailable'. Whatever you decide, it's best to be honest with yourself about why you are making the decision, and to take note when any publication, program, event or individual makes you feel uncomfortable.

Being asked to comment on things you don't know about

...

Always strongly consider declining to make public statements about things you don't actually know about, haven't been briefed on, or have no experience of. If you aren't sure about the topic, the question or what you are really being asked, avoid making up an answer.

I certainly don't mean to suggest that you need to be a fully qualified expert in every topic you speak out on, or even to suggest that every qualified expert knows *everything* about their field. That's just it – not even experts have an answer for everything. But many people in the public eye regularly find themselves pressed to comment on issues that are not in their field of expertise.

> There is no harm in saying that you don't know about something, particularly if it isn't in your field of knowledge.

There are a couple of reasons why this issue comes up so often in the media in particular. One of them is the popularity of panels of commentators on TV and radio who are asked to comment on different subjects every weekday. Often these people only know what they'll be talking about just before the segment goes to air, or at the most a few hours beforehand. I know this, because I have been there. Occasionally subjects will also come up that they have *no* time to prepare for, which means they can't research the topic or even give themselves a moment to think about their position. If the panellists are lucky, they have some prior knowledge of the subject, or they may have managed to read up on it beforehand because it was front-page news. (Reading the daily news in depth, and formulating positions on issues that may or may not come up, becomes an important practice to many public commentators.) If they are not lucky – or if the viewers are not lucky – they will not have been given any time, but will still be urged to make statements on the subject on live TV. This can lead to misinformation, and in some cases very ill-chosen statements that can haunt the speaker for some time.

The other reason why this is an important issue is the popularity of opinion pieces and columns that are produced with tight deadlines. I read a lot of these opinion pieces, and I have even written some, but the problem with many of them – and this is something many opinion writers themselves speak about – is that anyone hired as a columnist or opinion writer constantly needs to come up with new topics within a very short timeframe. Sometimes, topics that are outside their field of expertise will be all but forced on them by editors keen to cover a particularly hot issue. This naturally means they end up straying into areas outside their knowledge and have to write about them without the time to do proper research. If they get it really wrong it can be detrimental to their career and credibility, and it can also spread misinformation, sometimes harmful misinformation.

The best way to avoid scenarios like this is to simply say that you don't know, you don't have that information at present, you haven't looked into it or it is not your area of expertise. If it is a question you realise you *should* know the answer to, you may have some work ahead of you, but regardless, being honest is better than fudging a reply that turns out to be plain wrong.

There is no harm in saying that you don't know about something, particularly if it isn't in your field of knowledge. There can, however, be harm in making ill-conceived statements about issues just because you were asked to comment on them unprepared.

Saying no to questions

...

In the best of lives, there is a lot of 'yes' – saying yes to being open to other human beings; saying yes to new opportunities, new experiences, learning new things or re-learning the old; testing your abilities and pushing further, and standing up again when you fall. 'Yes' is part of what makes a life full and interesting, and it is something that successful people, change-makers and risk-takers say often.

There are also times to say 'no', or simply not respond.

In the arena of publicly speaking out, saying no is a right that sometimes needs reinforcement, particularly when you're made to feel that you are simply expected to say yes. Just because you have agreed to speak on a particular program, or speak out about a certain topic, does not mean no holds are barred, or no question is too invasive or personal. You *can* say no.

Here are just some of the reasons why you may find yourself saying no. (You might also want to take a look at the information on **setting boundaries** on pages 174 to 175.)

Invasive or inappropriate questions

Sometimes when speaking out, we will be faced with questions that for one reason or another 'step over the line' – they are too personal and invasive, or simply inappropriate. This can happen to anyone, no matter how high their rank or status. For example, in 2013 then Australian Prime Minister Julia Gillard was repeatedly asked by radio host Howard Sattler about the sexuality of her long-time partner Tim Mathieson because 'he's a hairdresser'. She told him that was absurd, but he soldiered on, pressing again and again with 'He's gay?', and asking for confirmation that her boyfriend was straight.[1]

On the book tour for *The Fictional Woman*, a book in which I discussed a sexual assault I survived 20 years earlier, I was asked live on TV if I bore my rapist any 'ill will'. I found the question surprising and inappropriate, particularly considering that about a dozen women in two countries came forward with claims against him at the time, and he showed little remorse at the trial, which saw him jailed for two years. What could I say? That I felt 'goodwill' towards such a person? Instead I responded, 'I think we probably shouldn't go there.'[2] I had decided to speak out about it in a book that was about a variety of issues facing women and girls. That didn't make me Mother Theresa. It was hardly an ambush – I suspect the interviewer had not thought about the question before she asked it, but it was still uncomfortable. This kind of thing can easily happen, particularly in live interviews.

When speaking out, we are all sometimes put on the spot by questions we should not have to answer, whether it is part of a planned ambush or not. If it happens to you, know that you are under no obligation to respond or, for that matter, to stay for the rest of the interview if you don't want to. I'm a stayer (so far), but many celebrities and others are not.

Whether it is a radio interview, job interview or just a private conversation, ultimately it is up to you to decide whether you want to answer a question. Just because you have agreed to be there, does not mean you have agreed to answer anything that is asked. The choice is still yours.

Personally triggering questions

As the anecdote just above would suggest, after *The Fictional Woman* came out I found myself asked a lot of public and personal questions about the sexual assault I had experienced. I had been prepared to answer some questions about it – I knew that was inevitable even though it was one page out of over 300 on many topics – but after some interviews I found myself shaking uncontrollably. Some were triggering. (A trigger can be defined as 'something that sets off a *memory tape* or flashback transporting the person back to the event of her/his original *trauma*'[3] or 'something that subconsciously switches us into feeling like we are reliving a past event'[4]) After my decades of media experience, fortunately, this was not often noticeable on camera, or in my voice on radio, but it would usually take me a couple of hours to recover. On one occasion, after a couple of particularly triggering interviews, I had to pull out of further media interviews for the day. Usually the interviews that caused this reaction were the ones where I was not warned beforehand about the line of questioning (I had written a book about women's issues, feminism, stereotypes and many life experiences, after all, not a book about one harrowing experience 20 years ago), or the interviewer was not well versed in sensitive reporting, and probed into intimate personal details like 'How did it *feel*?', 'Where is your rapist *now*?', and the one I quoted earlier: 'Do you bear him any *ill will*?'

I would often respond to unnecessarily personal and triggering questions by saying 'I think you can guess that it wasn't pleasant' and so on, but these kinds of live interviews took a toll. The point is, you are a human being, you have rights, and you don't have to answer anything you don't want to. What is triggering to one person is not necessarily triggering to the next person, and the reality is, sometimes interviewers will ask you questions they haven't thought through themselves, especially when the interview is live.

Alison Braun appeared on the TV weight-loss show *The Biggest Loser*, then her husband sadly took his life shortly afterwards. She told me that she was asked on more than one occasion whether she thought her husband had killed himself because she had lost a lot of weight.

Think about what that means to a bereaved widow. That you killed your husband? Through your own weight loss? It is beyond belief, and yet she was faced with such questions regularly, and in public.

It is important to know that there is no requirement to give intimate details in any individual interview, or to answer any particular question, even if you have said yes to these kinds of requests before. There is no requirement for an interviewee, let alone a victim of crime, to repeat the intimate details of their story, except in a legal context for the purposes of police and court proceedings.

As domestic violence campaigner and 2015 Australian of the Year Rosie Batty explained to me, 'Without realising, in the early stages of my journey I think I used the media as therapy. You find yourself wanting to talk. I'm lucky that intuitively I don't like trashy magazines. I spoke to journalists who have a reputation and who report in a sensitive manner.'

Sometimes, when asked again about how it 'felt' to have her son murdered by her former partner, she would find herself deeply affected. She told me:

> [I'm asked a question, and then] I realise I've become really upset. I don't want to go over the past with the same personal questions. It's not the fault of the journalists. I say, 'I'm not going to go there.' Sometimes they'll push, but they'll pipe down when asked to …
>
> Moving forward, I keep thinking about what I'm trying to do. I'm not trying for fame and fortune. I don't want sensationalised media that is really not about learning about an issue, just confronting people. That kind of program doesn't sit well with me, so why would I want to see myself on it? It's really important to choose the forms of media. What is their intent? I would ask them, what is your intention? I have gone past the really deep and personal questions. You know what, I answered all of those, I've moved on.

While we all want a life and career with a lot of 'yes', there will be times when you will want to say no. Knowing when to say no can be as valuable as knowing when to say yes. Whether an opportunity is unfairly unpaid, an organisation or publication makes you uncomfortable, or a question is inappropriate or overly personal, never forget it is your right to say no.

Knowing how and when to say 'no' in work or public life comes easier to some of us than to others. I see this skill as particularly important for women who have been told that they shouldn't say 'no', or don't have the right to, or those who have been taught to believe they should be grateful for any opportunity, regardless of the finer details. As much as saying 'yes' is important, learning when to say 'no' can be a valuable acquired skill.

CHAPTER 10

SPEAKING YOUR TRAUMA

Speaking out from personal experience

...

For many, speaking from personal experience can be an integral part of speaking out. When that involves speaking about a traumatic event or series of events, it can be both a powerful and a challenging experience for the speaker.

Take some time to consider your story, how it relates to the experiences of others and what you hope to achieve by speaking out about it. Many personal experiences – like miscarriage, sexual assault and child abuse – have what I call a toxic silence surrounding them, and that silence can have a negative impact on people who have been through them. Sharing your story with others who can relate to or have experienced similar things can help to reduce stigma and promote understanding of an issue. Nevertheless, speaking out about trauma can be psychologically complex and difficult, as we touched on briefly in the previous chapter. It can bring surprising responses that even the best prepared person can find challenging, frustrating, hurtful or even plain offensive. Extra self-care is required. (See **Chapter 15: Self-care**.)

Domestic violence spokeswoman Rosie Batty is one of the most extraordinary examples of a person taking a personal loss and using it for good. Doing media or public talks or fundraising for domestic or family

> Sharing your story with others who can relate to or have experienced similar things can help to reduce stigma and promote understanding of an issue.

> Speaking out about personal trauma and tragedy can bring surprising responses that even the best prepared person can find challenging, frustrating, hurtful or even plain offensive.

violence issues (something Rosie has done hundreds of times) can be challenging, particularly when that involves reliving your own loss and suffering by telling your story, as Rosie explains:

I just get very overwhelmed sometimes and just trapped, and I feel bombarded. You want to be polite or friendly, but at the same time you want to be able to go to the toilet, or you are about to go on stage. It's about realising what you need. I need some quiet time. I need some quiet time when I come off the stage, to just come down from the adrenaline that happens on stage.

You need to put strategies in place for you. Have some support around you, especially when you are travelling. Have really good support and professional advice.

You will have intense times … You have to have your boundaries and that is incredibly difficult at times.

Some tips

...

If you are speaking out about personal trauma, here are some basic tips that can help:

1. Look after you

The most important thing is your own wellbeing. Don't let anyone else pressure you into either remaining silent, or speaking out, if you are not ready. Consider your personal health and safety, as well as your legal rights. The choice must be yours. Do what is right for *you*.

> Don't let anyone else pressure you into either remaining silent, or speaking out, if you are not ready.

2. Set boundaries

Set personal boundaries for telling your story when speaking out publicly. This is vitally important regardless of whether you are writing about your experience, speaking about your experience in a speech or being interviewed about your experience.

As an example, when speaking out publicly about my own experience of sexual assault, I choose not to name my attacker (though there are police and court records with such details). I also do not give a lot of personal intimate detail about what happened during the attack, but I focus instead on the basics of the events leading up to and following the attack. I prefer to be referred to as a survivor, not a victim, as that is how I view myself now, years after the event. (Others prefer different terms.)

I set out those parameters before any interview that is likely to touch on the subject of the assault (though that is not always easy to anticipate, as I have mentioned). If an interviewer delves into personal details of my assault without warning, I change the subject or openly refuse to participate in that particular line of questioning. If an interviewer oversteps the boundaries we have set before the interview, or I just do not feel comfortable with the questions posed – one can never entirely anticipate what will be asked – I may say something like, 'I am not comfortable talking about that.' (Also see **Invasive or inappropriate questions** on pages 165 to 166, and **Personally triggering questions** on pages 166 to 168.) This can be done respectfully and most interviewers will understand.

Remember that just because you have agreed to talk about something doesn't mean that you have agreed to answer all possible personal questions about it. Boundaries are healthy. It is your right to decline to answer any questions or to end any interview.

> Do not underestimate the impact of speaking about traumatic personal experiences.

3. Practise

If you can, rehearse your speech or interview with a trusted friend. If you are going to be interviewed, have your friend ask you difficult questions, even questions you will refuse to answer. If you find this emotionally difficult, that is totally normal. At the same time, practising may help you feel more confident and in control before speaking out, and may help you to think of possible questions or answers you had not previously considered.

Be aware that some professional interviewers will spend a lot of time getting you to relax by asking general questions. They will then ask you the toughest, most potentially traumatising questions right at the end of the interview, and may only use your answers to those final questions. This is a common technique.

4. Be in a place where you feel safe

Traumatic experiences involve a feeling of not being safe. It is therefore particularly important to make sure you are in a safe and comfortable space when you retell that story. Some people find it helps to be somewhere familiar, but in all cases it is vital that you feel physically safe.

5. Have support at hand

Have a support person there for you, if at all possible. In most cases that support person will be there just to listen – tell them this – but if you show signs of distress or want to stop the interview they can help advocate for you.

Do not underestimate the impact of speaking about traumatic personal experiences. Having a support person nearby can become important, and frankly, having a friend take you out for a chat or a drink afterwards can be a real relief.

6. Be in control

When you are in control of the narrative, in control of telling your own story, you are less likely to feel re-traumatised by telling that story. Speak honestly and in your own words, staying within the personal boundaries you have set. Remember that once your story is out, it may be interpreted and retold by others, sometimes selectively – which brings me back to my first point: always consider your personal safety, health, wellbeing and legal rights. Speaking out on personal issues can be powerful and important, but the choice must be yours.

> When you are in control of the narrative, in control of telling your own story, you are less likely to feel re-traumatised by telling that story.

An example scenario

This is a distressing scenario to imagine, but it is something some survivors face, and it illustrates some of the points we have gone over.

Let's say you are a woman severely injured by your husband. You are hospitalised, your husband is jailed and you divorce. You later choose to speak out about your experience of abuse and you are offered money by a magazine to tell your story. Speaking out will raise awareness about domestic violence and the money will help you support your children as a single parent.

Here are some things to consider, using the tips we have discussed:

What is the publication? Is it a publication you are familiar and comfortable with? If you don't know it, look at a few copies and consider whether you would want to appear in it.

What is the publication hoping to get for their money? Are there particular things they want? Exclusivity? Photos? Certain personal details? You should find out what those are.

What is in the contract you have been asked to sign? Read it carefully. Get legal advice if possible. Are there any clauses that need changing? (See the next point.)

What are your personal boundaries? Are there
any parts of your story that are off limits? Will the
magazine get access to images of your children or other
family members, and want to publish those? Will your
children's names or images be altered to protect their
privacy? Will the magazine get access to police reports
or images of your injuries? Will they try to interview
your former husband? If any of these are no-go areas,
and/or could affect you or your children in terms of
health, safety or employment, those areas should be
flagged immediately and included in the contract.
The more specific the contract and the more of your
correspondence that is in writing, the more likely you
are to be happy with the results of the interview, and
the more likely you will be to have legal recourse if
something goes very wrong. Likewise, the more things
are spelled out and made clear to all parties involved,
the more likely the publication will be happy with the
results. It is better for everyone.

Speaking publicly about sexual violence

...

Speaking out about the trauma of sexual violence brings its own challenges, some of which I am familiar with. When your personal story of sexual violence makes its way into the mainstream press, or when your speaking out involves sharing your story with the press, you can feel as if it is out of your control and has become 'public property'. Sometimes it becomes twisted and warped.

The experience where some members of the media fail to respect your privacy or boundaries is familiar to me, both as an unknown young woman and later as a person with a public profile. Had media organisations in the UK and US in the 1990s not taken it upon themselves to publicly publish the names of the accusers before the trial of the serial rapist who attacked me – putting me and all the other victims/survivors at risk – I would never have been publicly linked to the case. The only link would have remained where it belonged: on a police database and in court documents. As it was, my name was printed multiple times as that of a 'rape victim', despite my choosing never to speak to the press about it. My father was hounded for images of me – this was before Facebook or even Google – and even offered large sums for images or comment. (He refused.)

Almost two decades later I chose to write about the experience in *The Fictional Woman*, as a way of showing solidarity with other victims of crime. There were soon multiple headlines linking my name with the word 'rape', which can be a strange experience, and there were also headlines about my 'demons', my 'dark, tragic past', my 'shocking confession' etc. These are standard tabloid phrases, but

> Speaking out on personal issues can be powerful and important, but the choice must be yours.

the things they wrote about were *not* my demons. I had nothing to confess; I was not the one who did something wrong.

One article called 'What we can learn from Tara Moss's rapist'[1] is instructive for the way it demonstrates the way the public handling of personal stories can silence the victim/survivor, often unintentionally. The writer took quotes from another writer's article about *The Fictional Woman*, then wrote an entire piece about my rape experience without attempting to contact me, quote me, or even mention that the original article he quoted from was about a book I'd written. He did, however, publicly and prominently name the rapist and look him up for a quote. A large picture of the convicted rapist appeared at the top of the column. I was pictured with a caption that read 'Raped at 21: Tara Moss'. Meanwhile, I was relegated to voicelessness, talked *about* but not to, with two men, the writer and the rapist, given room to have their say. The unintended suggestion was that we can 'learn from' the rapist but not from the victim/survivor. Again, women are rendered unreliable witnesses of their own experiences. (The article was later voluntarily removed by the publication after they received numerous complaints about it from readers and journalists who found it unethical or inappropriate and said it 'should not have been published'.[2])

As a fiction writer, I understand the power of stories. I understand the importance of language. The voices we hear, the stories we share and the language we use matter. It is within our power as a community to do better in relation to sexual violence. We must make it easier and safer for survivors to speak out, because the voices of survivors of crime matter a great deal indeed. We must listen to them. Survivors are one of the main keys to understanding both the crimes themselves, and how to rebuild lives afterwards, and these are the voices that have too often been dismissed, to our collective detriment.

'Survivors are one of the main keys to understanding both the crimes themselves, and how to rebuild lives afterwards, and these are the voices that have too often been dismissed, to our collective detriment.'

For information on media best practice regarding reporting on or understanding the issues around sexual violence, see:

www.aifs.gov.au/acssa/media/mbh.html
dartcenter.org/topic/sexual-violence
www.rape-dvservices.org.au/
www.fullstopfoundation.org.au

CHAPTER 11

VICARIOUS TRAUMA

What is vicarious trauma?

...

Vicarious trauma is something I have learned a great deal about in recent years, and it is vital to discuss it in this book, because the topic will already be, or will soon become, relevant to many of you. Even if you don't know it yet.

First, let me take a quick step back and explain how vicarious trauma became such a big part of my world, to give you just one example of what it can look like, even though your experiences will be different from mine.

In 2014, after I published my partly autobiographical book *The Fictional Woman,* I was invited to appear on a panel on the current affairs TV program *Q&A.* I was asked by host Tony Jones why I had chosen to speak out about the experiences I'd related in chapter 3 of the book, of being stalked, attacked and sexually assaulted in my younger years (that this came up in numerous discussions of the book is something I have already discussed in **Chapters 9** and **10**). This is a transcript of how I responded on that occasion:

> What I found was that when you're talking about the experience of women and girls there are fictions that we hold – that things like sexual violence happen to *other* people. Things like miscarriage happen to *other* people. I'm someone who wants to be speaking out as an advocate for some of these issues for women and girls.
>
> I really felt like I couldn't talk about some of these issues for women and girls without talking about sexual violence and I couldn't talk about sexual violence without putting my hand up and showing solidarity with other victims of crime and saying, 'I'm one of you.'

I added that physical and sexual violence affects about one in three women. (One in three Australian women have experienced physical and/or sexual violence perpetrated by someone known to them, according to the Australian Bureau of Statistics[1] and worldwide, about 1 in 3 (35%) women have experienced either physical and/or sexual intimate partner violence or non-partner sexual violence in their lifetime, according to the World Health Organisation.[2]) Many men also experience sexual violence, and there would be people in the audience and at home who are affected by it.

> Vicarious trauma can have an impact on even the strongest and most 'prepared' person. Knowing what it is, and how you can manage it, can help.

I went on to say, 'I think there is a toxic silence surrounding this issue and we need to get a lot better at talking about it. And one of the reasons is because the silence protects the predators – it also shames the victims. It also robs us as a community of the tools to be able to support people adequately when these things happen to them ...'

As for being called 'brave' because I was speaking out, which had suddenly started happening once the book came out, the thing is, survivors of these types of crimes rarely hear that at the time, when they really need that support. I went on:

They don't tell you that at the time. They don't tell you you're brave, you're a role model, that you've survived something. They often tell you that you should be silent. They tell you that it's your fault. They tell you that you were asking for it, that you did something wrong.

Viewers at home: you will get through this. This will pass. You are strong. You do not need to be silent.

This spontaneous moment on the program prompted perhaps a thousand people to get in touch with me within a period of only a few days. For me, this was an unprecedented amount of contact from strangers in such a short period of time.

A few of the social media messages made personal rape and death threats – which is an important issue that I will discuss in the next chapter, **Unsocial Social Media**. But the vast majority sent heartfelt and supportive messages, and a large number of them also disclosed their own experiences of sexual assault, including gang rape, child abuse and intimate partner violence.

> While I had mentally prepared myself for most of the media reaction, I had not been fully prepared for the outpouring of support, emotion and personal stories from *ordinary people.*

Though there were fewer messages each day after that first week – hundreds instead of thousands, and later, down to perhaps a dozen a day – the experience remained intense. As Rosie Batty relays in the previous chapter, 'You will have intense times.' That was certainly true for me. As I travelled around the country I was often met with hugs from strangers, and would find that some people actually spontaneously burst into tears at seeing me. Often they explained that they were reading that particular chapter ('Chapter 3', I'd hear again and again), or they would tell me they had seen me on *Q&A* and had been particularly moved by what I'd said.

It was often a beautiful experience, if emotionally draining. And though I would not change a thing – not one word – the fact is that while I had mentally prepared myself for most of the *media reaction*, arming myself with statistics and info on the topics that might come up, I had not been fully prepared for the outpouring of support, emotion and personal stories from *ordinary people.*

I could not have imagined that from that moment on, there would be men and women telling me about the child abuse they had endured, sometimes right before I went on air to speak about the book; or that there would be readers telling me about the abusive relationships they had fled; and that there would be women and girls telling me about the abuse they were *currently experiencing* in their own homes, sometimes in book-signing line-ups, or on the street.

I listened to many stories knowing that these people were *not* safe yet, and that they needed someone to help them *right now*. Sometimes these people were underage, and that truly broke my heart. I wanted to take all those kids with me and make them feel safe ever afterwards.

But of course I could not. I could only refer them to professionals, who would do as much for them as they could. I could advise kids that what was happening was not their fault and they should speak to a trusted adult or call the Kids Helpline (1800 55 1800 in Australia). In the case of adults, I would mention the 1800 RESPECT free professional counselling service and recommend they speak to a counsellor or police officer about their experiences and what their options were as soon as possible.

I felt not only troubled by what these people were telling me, but I also felt inadequate because of how little I could do to help. I am someone who dedicates a lot of time to unpaid advocacy work in human rights and women's and children's rights, and who tries to stay informed. I attend conferences, read papers, speak to experts and pore over case studies and data. But that does not make me a qualified professional counsellor or psychologist. It doesn't make me a police officer or a judge.

I was never able to 'switch off' when I heard these stories as a psychologist or other professional learns to do. I did not have 'office hours' as it were. I would be confronted while doing my shopping or catching a train. My exposure to this trauma was usually random and unexpected.

Sometimes, because a person was in a book-signing line-up, or had somewhere else to be, the exchange I had with them would take only a few minutes from start to finish. It would happen with little or no warning, and no follow up, unless I had a way to contact them again. That was sometimes the hardest part – knowing there was no way I could possibly do more for them, and no way for me to know what would happen to them.

The experience left me more determined than ever to speak out on the issues of sexual assault and intimate partner violence, but ultimately I also found the avalanche of stories triggering.

This, I now realise, was inevitable. I found myself running on very little sleep over many months, even feeling panicked at times. I was trying to respond to every unexpected disclosure in the most responsible and human way possible. I wanted to make sure I was supportive and did not make things worse with a poorly chosen word or a distracted response in a signing line-up of hundreds of people. I wanted to respond to each email and social media message myself, particularly because so many of them were clearly heartfelt and deeply personal. It was a responsibility I felt honoured to be faced with. But it was a *lot* of responsibility and I was never able to do enough. After a few months, I'd lost several kilos, I was not sleeping and I was deeply wary of further triggering stories. In short, I was burning out.

This kind of experience is, as it turns out, not at all unusual. What I was experiencing was **vicarious trauma**.

I was trying to respond to every unexpected disclosure in the most responsible and human way possible ... I was burning out.

Support for vicarious trauma

...

Karen Willis is Executive Officer of Rape & Domestic Violence Services Australia, and has worked in the sector for over 35 years, providing frontline services for victims and survivors of sexual assault and domestic or intimate partner violence. She contacted me after I appeared on the show to see how I was doing, and to thank me for what I had done on air, showing solidarity with other survivors of crime and speaking out about a difficult topic that affects people of all genders, and in particular, a huge number of women and girls in Australia and around the world. The following year I became patron of the Full Stop Foundation, which supports their work, and which I launched at Parliament House.

Karen strongly suspected that I would benefit from learning more about vicarious trauma and self-care. And she was right.

Vicarious trauma is a major issue for advocates and other people in the sexual violence sector, and for anyone who hears highly distressing stories on a regular basis as part of their paid work or unpaid advocacy. This includes those who work as counsellors, police officers, paramedics, social workers and more.

'When people tell us about the violence they have experienced it is inevitable that their story will be distressing,' Karen explained. 'While we choose to do this work the personal cost can be high. This impact, called vicarious trauma, can be managed. That way we can stay well and keep doing the work we are committed to doing.

'Each client, regardless of what has happened, will at some stage express a hurt that is so deep in them and so painful. It is hard to really understand how someone [an abuser or rapist] can deliberately do that to someone else …'

I asked Karen how she handles vicarious trauma in her own life:

Firstly I recognise that I am only human and that the stories
and the emotions they generate will have an impact on me and
everyone else. Our workplace has a lot of practices in place to
manage this impact called vicarious trauma.

It is a WH&S [workplace health and safety] issue and we also
have a [personal] responsibility, it's not all up to the workplace.
I certainly make the best use of what the workplace offers, and
I also do things in my own life to make sure there is balance –
being with friends and family, doing things that have nothing to
do with work and that are fun or good for the soul, being aware if
my behaviours or thoughts begin to change and thinking about
why, and if it is about the work then doing something about it.

I have a great extended family network, and while sometimes
that can be a challenge all on its own, it is special to be part of
something like that. I also have some great friends. They are busy
women so we don't see each other all the time, but when we do it
is great.

My own work with UNICEF as their National Ambassador for Child
Survival can also be challenging at times, in different ways. As one
example, visiting several Syrian refugee camps in Lebanon in 2015
was a life-changing experience for me. I held kids we knew were
dying. I was at one camp when a devastating fire tore through another
camp just next to us, killing young children, all because of a simple
cooking accident. I saw families lining up for the meagre services
made available to them through charitable donations, knowing that
if they were in Australia, things would be so different for them – if
war had not broken out in their homeland, and they had not been
forced to flee because of circumstances beyond their control. Many
talked non-stop about their homes, their hopes of returning, their

longing for news of family members or whether their houses were still standing.

Faced with stories like these, it's hard not to feel guilty, inadequate. I have been a UNICEF ambassador since 2007. But this time, on the third day of my trip, I began to fall apart. I was unable to get myself together as I'd hoped to. I needed to take a break at one camp as a result, and that felt humiliating to me. I was glad that at least I'd held it together in front of the kids and families, but some of the other workers saw me in that vulnerable moment, when I couldn't stop crying.

It's the little details that sometimes make you crack. In this instance it was the reality that over a dozen small children had been electrocuted to death while walking or playing in a particular area of a camp with bad wiring. As a parent of a young child, I couldn't help but imagine what it would be like to be living in limbo with her somewhere in a camp, where it was that dangerous for my child. I lost it.

After sitting down in private, drinking some tea and using some tissues I picked myself up again and carried on. Fortunately I'd only slowed down our demanding schedule by 10 minutes, but I hated that I'd been unable to go on.

I kept it together again until I got back to my hotel that night. I was exhausted, dehydrated (despite my best efforts) from the soaring temperatures and hot tents, and again, I fell apart trying to process what I'd seen. It can happen to anyone. It wasn't even the worst scenario I was exposed to on that trip. But that was another part of it: I knew I'd only gained security clearance for the 'safer' areas. I knew it got far worse in other areas, and yet the things I'd seen were things I'll never forget.

I can judge myself harshly sometimes, and in that moment I felt inadequate and weak – my tears weren't going to help those families – but they needed to come out anyway. After that, I was stronger. I am human, after all.

It takes a special kind of strength to do this work on a regular basis, as foreign aid workers and my colleagues at UNICEF do. As Kate Moore from UNICEF explains:

> My colleagues and I see a lot of the bad, bad things that happen to children, their families and their communities. It's true, there have been times I have noticed in my peers a sense of despair or distress as images flood through from our friends and colleagues in the field, or as we worry for changing community attitudes toward people who are vulnerable and need us to be compassionate for them. It's really OK to say you're angry, or upset, or distressed, and that you need a moment. If you are mentally and emotionally drained and fatigued, you can't be your best self – and the people we're advocating for really need us to be our best selves. These people, often children, are already emotionally and very often physically wrecked. They need strong supporters who can champion their needs, so taking a moment to build yourself back up really is nothing if you're prepared to play the long game.

Vicarious trauma will be relevant for many readers of this book. Speaking out often involves speaking out for others in difficult circumstances, or speaking out about our own difficult experiences, which (as I discovered) can in turn attract a lot of disclosures about similar experiences from others, often in unexpected moments. Vicarious trauma can have an impact on even the strongest and most 'prepared' person. Knowing what it is, and how you can manage it, can help.

Understanding and responding to vicarious trauma

The following information (pages 193 to 198) is provided by Rape & Domestic Violence Services Australia, who have an award-winning Vicarious Trauma Management program.

What is vicarious trauma?

Vicarious trauma is the negative impact of being exposed to traumatic content, such as hearing stories about traumatic events people have experienced.

What does vicarious trauma look like?

Symptoms of vicarious trauma generally fall into three categories:

- Re-experiencing (intrusive thoughts, nightmares, flashbacks)
- Avoidance (of people, places and feelings, or blocking out things using alcohol or drugs)
- Hyper or chronic arousal (on edge, anxiety, disturbed sleep).

Vicarious trauma can also change the way people feel about themselves and about others:

- Esteem ('I deserve good things in life', 'Other people's help/input is valuable')
- Trust ('I am a trustworthy person', 'Other people are generally trustworthy')

- Control ('I'm not worried about losing control of my emotions or behaviour, 'I feel OK when other people are in charge')
- Intimacy ('I don't mind spending time alone', 'I feel connected to other people')
- Safety ('I am safe', 'The people I care about are safe').

Near-miss story

This story is about a practitioner who worked as a generalist counsellor for three years before she took a role as a trauma specialist counsellor for Rape & Domestic Violence Services Australia. When she started work as a sexual assault counsellor, she was keen and interested and felt fine. However, after a few months she started to realise that something wasn't right. She was starting to worry about her personal safety, which was unusual for her. She would start to check that doors were locked, that windows were shut tight and that someone would always stay at home with her. Once a month her husband worked nights; this started to impact on her relationships, as she was always trying to convince her friends to stay over. The counsellor realised that she was experiencing symptoms of vicarious trauma, as previously she had never really worried about personal safety. She realised that listening to stories that were trauma-related was having a negative impact on her. She informed her supervisor and they developed a self-care management plan to manage the symptoms and work though her feelings of safety in her external counselling sessions.

Direct hit story

Lucy was in her forties when she decided to train as a social worker. She had worked as a hairdresser for over 20 years and felt that she wanted to do something that was more altruistic. She took out a Higher Education Contribution Scheme loan and spent the next four years studying to be a social worker. She was delighted when she passed her course and she soon began work as a child protection case worker. However, after a year, she started to experience difficulties and began to have a lot of time off work. One day when she was travelling to court with a colleague, her colleague noticed a map on the passenger car floor. Lucy had made a map of a route from the office to court and the map had lots of red dots on it. The colleague was perplexed and asked her why she needed a map, as they always travelled to court and she could find it with her eyes shut! Lucy confessed that she was really struggling to cope and that she needed a map to identify toilet stops on the way, as she often felt sick or needed to go to the toilet. The colleague didn't follow up on this issue with Lucy or with Lucy's supervisor. Shortly after, Lucy left her role as a social worker and went on long-term sick leave, submitting a workers compensation claim. The cost to this woman was enormous: she incurred financial hardship and a deterioration in her relationships and spent four years training in a profession that she could no longer work in.

Managing symptoms of vicarious trauma

Symptoms vary from a minimal impact on a person's life to a severe impact. The aim is to keep symptoms manageable, close to minimal impact, by addressing symptoms early. There are five strategies that should be used to manage symptoms effectively:

1. Education

Learning about vicarious trauma, or training for your workplace.

2. Reduce risk

Leave work at work by debriefing or doing a grounding activity.

Exercise: Debrief with a colleague by answering these questions:

- What was your shift like?
- Did any of the information impact you?
- What are you planning on doing to leave it at work?

Alternative exercises when debrief isn't possible:

- Answer the debrief questions in an email sent to yourself
- Listen to the radio in the car on the way home to ground yourself.

3. Monitor symptoms

Measure symptoms using questionnaires:

Google: Compassion Fatigue Self Test by Charles Figley

Check in with yourself:

Exercise: How do you know if you might be experiencing vicarious trauma?

Write down your 'dominant emotion' 10 days in a row – do you feel 'hopeful'? 'frustrated'? 'anxious'?

It's normal for the dominant emotion to vary most days. If it's a negative emotion that is similar most days, there may be an issue that could be explored with a counsellor.

Daily monitoring:
- 'Eyeball' your colleagues – do they look stressed?
- Checking in with your colleagues – are they OK?
- Talk about vicarious trauma in the workplace.

4. Early intervention for symptoms
- Access a supervisor for debrief after trauma exposure (24/7)
- 1800RESPECT is available for support managing vicarious trauma (in Australia).

5. Offsetting symptoms
- Self-care
- Access an external supervisor who specialises in vicarious trauma.

Symptom	It might look like	These activities might help
Re-experiencing	Intrusive thoughts, nightmares, flashbacks	Grounding based on the type of impact (sight, hearing, touch, smell, taste): • A visually creative activity helps to clear a nasty mental picture • Listening to music to clear an audio recall • Playing with a puppy; stroking a cat
Avoidance	Staying away from certain people or places, avoiding feelings by blocking out things using alcohol or drugs	• Arrange to spend time with other people • Consider talking with a counsellor about how you feel
Hyper or chronic arousal	On edge, anxiety, disturbed sleep	• Physical activities (swimming, walking) • Creative activities (beading, knitting)

Final thoughts on vicarious trauma

...

Rosie Batty, domestic violence campaigner, 2015 Australian of
the Year:

> I tried to be accessible to everyone, and try to help everyone, but
> I can't cope with the volume of the people trying to contact me,
> and the intense expectation that I am going to save their life …
> I have had my fair share of PTSD [post-traumatic stress disorder].
> I've always had a journey of recognising my emotional space,
> when I need the company of good friends, or counselling. I had
> to, from the beginning, due to confronting hate mail, kind of
> detach myself. Initially I tried to answer the emails myself. Now I
> have someone helping me. I know it is inadequate. I am unable to
> intervene with [individual] victim journeys … I am advocating for
> systemic change, and I use those victim stories in a confidential
> way, to make change, to make those stories heard. I wish I could
> do more. It has been incredibly overwhelming. I am not working
> at that crisis frontline place. I see my place as advocating.
> Certainly I have a lot of victim contact, but it's mainly people
> recognising I want people's voices and stories to be heard …
> I work out ways to feel like I'm still making a difference.

CHAPTER 12

UNSOCIAL SOCIAL MEDIA

Speaking out in our digital world

...

A lot of our interaction with the world – both private communications and speaking out publicly – is now performed digitally, from e-book, blogs, social media posts, the comments sections under news articles, and other forms of electronic publishing, to instant messaging, texts and emails. Technology has created exciting new opportunities as well as new challenges, and has changed the day to day experiences of most people under 70 (and many over 70). In fact, 90% of Australian women say they are online for at least one hour every day, usually many more[1], and even 40% of women over the age of 60 now report spending at least 3 hours a day online. People of all ages now use online spaces and digital communication as an integral part of their social lives, their work lives and their means of staying informed, and to access goods, services, entertainment and more.

My daughter is too young to use the internet just yet – or spell – but like the majority of children today she is already very aware of the fact that her parents have devices they talk into and navigate with their fingertips. Perhaps she is doubly aware of this having writers for parents. Keypads and iPads are therefore a source of fascination – and some danger, with the quick fingers of children and that delete button.

I remember her at a relative's house touching a TV screen for the first time, and seeing if she could make the pictures on it move with her fingers. It was then I realised, undeniably, that children today would be acquainted with technology in a way none of us could have anticipated just 10 years ago. On a recent trip to

> Technology has created exciting new opportunities as well as new challenges, and has changed the day to day experiences of most people under 70 (and many over 70).

Syrian refugee camps (see **Chapter 11**) I watched as mobile medical doctors used iPads to log important patient data in the most remote locations. Many refugee families had fled with little more than the clothes on their backs – and their mobile phones. Across continents, cultures and the extremes of human experience, technology and connectivity are all but inescapable.

> Gone are the days when the reading public might send a handwritten missive via a publisher, which would take days or even months to reach an author.

Like many, I am acquainted with the online world in ways I could not previously have imagined. Gone are the days when the reading public might send a handwritten missive via a publisher, which would take days or even months to reach an author. Now messages come in real time to the device in your back pocket, often in 140 characters. And the tone of some of those messages has, from anecdotal evidence at least, changed dramatically in recent years.

'Cyberhate'

...

Dr Emma A. Jane from the University of New South Wales is leading a three-year, federal government-funded study into the impact of 'gendered cyberhate' on women. Her preliminary findings indicate there has been a distinct change in both the volume of hate directed at women online, and the type of rhetoric used. Dr Jane told me:

> Strongly held views expressed via strongly worded missives have always been part of the internet experience. Since about 2011, however, these messages have become far more prevalent, far more graphic and far more threatening in terms of hyperbolic descriptions of exactly how a woman will be gang-raped, mutilated, killed and so on. In fact, this type of 'e-bile' has been normalised to the point where rape threats have become the 'go-to' approach for men who disagree with women – especially if this disagreement happens to involve gender equity and feminism.

When I spoke on TV panel show *Q&A* in solidarity with other sexual assault survivors (see **Chapter 13**), it led to graphic death and rape threats on Twitter – hidden like razor blades among hundreds of heartfelt messages of support from both men and women. It was hardly my first or last experience of this kind. Nor is my experience unique. The following year a group of high-profile women read out some of the messages they regularly get online in a video put together by the website *Mamamia*, including tweets like this one, received by Australian journalist Tracey Spicer: 'I hope your children are raped and killed, you silly c**t.' In recent years I've noticed that many messages are almost identical in content. To quote Dr Jane's words, 'this type of "e-bile" has been normalised'.

Caroline Criado-Perez is a feminist and activist who has successfully taken on the Bank of England to get novelist Jane Austen pictured on 10 pound notes. 'I had absolutely no idea I would get rape and death threats for suggesting we should put pictures of women on banknotes,' she says. 'I felt it was my duty not to be cowed and not to shut up. I felt it was important to set an example; it was also a bit of bloody-mindedness – why on earth would you give trolls what they want?'[2]

Writer, activist and proud Arrernte woman Celeste Liddle explains:

> I think the major problem with trolls is that, like everything else in society, the broader public reaction tends to be to blame the victim. We put ourselves out there, so apparently we deserve what comes back at us. And this is particularly the case when you are a racially marginalised woman. People absolutely feel they have the right to send gendered and racist abuse directly to you because you stuck your head above the parapet. I wish I could say growing a thick skin is the answer, but if anything I've found that maintaining my online space as an Indigenous feminist space that does not tolerate abuse, and blocking those who contravene this outright, has been my best way of dealing with it. It's nice to think that such types have spaces online where they are completely irrelevant and don't have a right to be there, because generally they feel quite self-entitled.

Unsocial social media is everywhere, sadly, and for many women who speak out, blocking and banning become necessary parts of the online experience.

Unsocial social media is everywhere, sadly, and for many women who speak out, blocking and banning become necessary parts of the online experience.

Though women in the public eye have been found to cop a particularly high rate of violent abuse, at least half of all women experience abuse online. I helped design a survey into online abuse carried out in February 2016 by the security company Norton, called

Online Harassment: The Australian Woman's Experience.[3] The results showed that 47% of Australian women of all ages have been subjected to online harassment, rising to 76% of women under 30. The majority of those surveyed also believed that online abuse was a major problem and had become worse since the previous year.

Although men and women receive roughly equal amounts of abuse, the nature of the abuse is often different, with women far more likely to be threatened with rape and death, and subjected to online sexual harassment, cyberstalking, revenge porn and sextortion. About one in six Australian women under 30 reported that among their worst online experiences, they have received death threats – about twice the number of men in the same age group. In addition, one in ten women have experienced graphic sexual harassment, rising to one in five women under 30, and one in seven women have experienced threats of physical violence online, rising to a quarter of women under 30. Shockingly, one in ten Australian women under 30 have already been the victim of revenge porn or sextortion, both extreme breaches of privacy, and crimes.

Revenge porn is a crime. Sextortion is a crime. Threats of death, rape or other physical harm are illegal online, just as they are offline. Likewise, it is against the law to encourage a person to harm themselves. As I have said elsewhere,[4] many times, *this is not a matter of free speech, it is a matter of public safety and law*. Though these types of crimes are not always reported, or when reported do not always result in adequate support or action, it is against the law. Perpetrators have been jailed. It is never okay. We must stand up to it, and we can't simply leave the internet to the bullies. Over half (56%) of survey respondents felt that better online security measures were needed, and that the police and authorities needed to start taking victims more seriously (58%). As a community we need to do more to acknowledge the real effects of online abuse and take a firm stand against it, and as with offline abuse, we need to make reporting safer and easier.

Many women cope with abuse, 'e-bile' and threats online by blocking or banning (I block early and often) and adjusting their privacy settings, but for others who cop a lot of personal abuse, avoiding online comments and some social media sites entirely becomes a strategy for coping, as campaigner against family violence and founder of the Luke Batty Foundation, Rosie Batty notes:

> It can be incredibly confronting and upsetting, so I don't read Facebook and I don't look at the comments online. I did [at first], and then you find yourself wanting to respond and you get drawn in. You can't take it personally. The only people you need to keep in touch with are the people who know you and are informed. It is really important to look at your safety and security, so you don't feel your personal space is jeopardised.

You don't need to be female to be on the receiving end of e-bile or online threats, either – they are received by all genders, and include race hate, 'fat shaming', and hate aimed at minority groups such as those who identify as lesbian, gay, bisexual, transgender, intersex or queer (LGBTIQ). A 2013 Gay, Lesbian and Safe Education Network (GLSEN) study, *Out Online*, suggests LGBTIQ youth experience almost three times as much bullying and harassment online as their straight peers.

While some online harassment is random, many trolls and abusers use personal information – to do with race, gender, sexual orientation, disability and life history – to play on and amplify perceived vulnerabilities. It's one thing to be called an unpleasant name online. It's another thing to receive a barrage of abuse that involves triggering information and personal details, and another thing again when technology is used to maliciously pry into and broadcast aspects of your private life, including your place of residence, information about your family and so on.

Online harm can come from strangers, and indeed, some of the most terrifying barrages of cyberhate come from groups of strangers working together to bully someone. But for many, the worst actually comes from people they know. In recent years there hasn't been one school I've spoken at in my capacity as a writer or cyber safety advocate that has *not* been visited by the spectre of cyberbullying, often with tragic results. Bullying is one known risk factor in depression, and tragically, suicide kills almost twice as many kids as our roads.

In addition to illuminating the extent of the problem of online abuse, the Norton survey of women's online experiences revealed the toll on women's mental health – 20% of those surveyed felt violated or abused by their experience of online abuse, 9% had their work or studies impacted by online abuse, 9% needed to seek professional help for depression and/or anxiety, and a disturbing 5% felt suicidal. These are real messages, sent by real people and the impacts on their targets are very real.

> The internet is a powerful tool. Like anything powerful, it can be used as a weapon.

The internet is a powerful tool. Like anything powerful, it can be used as a weapon.

Technology has opened up valuable new ways to speak out and be heard, to find help and support, to share experiences, get published or gain access to previously difficult-to-find material. Unfortunately technology is also used to shame, bully and brutalise. Though some social media sites are adopting better reporting methods and the law is starting to take online abuse more seriously, there is a long way to go. Even the strongest, most intelligent and experienced woman or girl may still find herself pushed to the wall. Arming yourself with knowledge about social media and digital spaces can help you to more confidently and safely negotiate these spaces, both privately and when choosing to speak out to a public audience online.

A basic glossary of internet terms

Here are some basic terms you should know and some potential online crimes you should be aware of. **NOTE:** definitions for some of these terms vary. Some of the definitions below contain disturbing content.

Banning/blocking

The denial of electronic access to parts of the web. For instance, on social media platforms a user can be blocked from seeing your feed, posting on your page or sending you messages. (Be aware that they may log off and search for your page to see your feed, or start a new account to send you messages.) Users may also be blocked from access to various websites, user groups, or areas of the internet.

Cyberbullying

Deliberately bullying, harassing, threatening, intimidating, humiliating or otherwise intending to harm someone through electronic communications, including (but not limited to) emails, mobile phone messages, apps, social media or chat room messages. This term is often used in relation to young people but also applies to the adult community. There is no reason to believe that this electronic bullying is less harmful than bullying in the physical world, particularly as digital technology allows the bully to amplify and broadcast their messages or attacks, and easily enlist others to join in. It's important to know that cyberbullying can be a crime, and cyberbullies can do time.

Cyberstalking

Stalking a person online or using digital technology, often including repeated harassment, intimidation and intrusion on a person's privacy.

Cyberthreats

Threatening electronic messages or posts, or any electronic material that raises concerns that the author intends to do harm to others or themselves.

Doxing

An abbreviation of 'dropping docs (documents)'. Doxing or doxxing is the dangerous internet-based practice of researching private, identifying information about someone and broadcasting that information publicly without consent. This may include broadcasting a person's private address, place of work, phone number or credit card details, names of family members and more. This is generally done with the aim of causing harm, crossing personal boundaries, shattering expectations of privacy and intimidating the target. It can also have the aim of giving out identifying information to help others join in the harassment of that person. (See box, **Tips for protecting your personal information**, on pages 223 to 225.)

Exclusion

Intentionally and maliciously excluding someone from an online group or game they might reasonably have expected to take part in. This has recently been called a digital form of schoolyard bullying.

Flaming

Posting rude, obscene or angry messages in an online group, on social media, or privately through email or SMS. (This term is no longer commonly used.)

Happy slapping

An extreme form of criminal bullying where physical assaults are recorded and the footage distributed, sometimes being posted on social media sites or elsewhere online. This is often intended to humiliate the person assaulted, but also means the footage can be used as evidence and lead to criminal charges against the perpetrators and distributors.

Revenge porn

Nude or sexually explicit images or videos distributed without the consent of the subject. This extreme form of online attack or 'revenge' is reportedly on the rise, perpetrated by ex-partners as a form of intimate partner abuse, as well as being a wider phenomenon, with hackers using technology to spread intimate images without consent. Most but not all victims of revenge porn are women and girls. Revenge porn is illegal. (See more under **Know the law, know your rights** below.) If a person has not explicitly consented, do not distribute a nude, intimate or otherwise personal image. Ever. If you have reason to believe that the person has not consented to the use of their image, **do not view it, save it or circulate it**.

Sexting

Put simply, this form of communication uses the same technology as texting, only the content is sexual in nature – be it words or pictures. It is important to note that, legally speaking, the pictures that are sent can qualify as child pornography if the subject is underage. (See **Online safety** on pages 218 to 222.)

Sextortion

A situation where someone is blackmailed for money or sexual favours by a person threatening to publish compromising sexual images or information about their sex life.

Sock puppet

This is a fake online account set up by the author of a blog or post that defends the author of a blog or post, while pretending not to be that person.

Swatting

Incredibly, there is a growing problem, largely in the US, with people who make malicious false reports to the police with the aim of having a heavily armed SWAT (Special Weapons and Tactics) team sent to the target's home. 'Swatters' often use cheap technology to make the false reports while disguising their own identity. Swatting is illegal, may result in unintended harm or death for one or more of the targets or police officers, and diverts important and expensive resources from genuine emergency situations.

Trolling

The term 'troll' is overused, and trolling behaviour is sadly even more overused. An online troll is usually defined as a person intentionally posting offensive, rude or angry messages or false information online with the aim of upsetting or 'baiting' people, in order to create conflict or distress, and/or to derail discussions.

Trolling – Concern troll

This subcategory of troll isn't always as easy to spot. This is a person who posts in online groups or forums, falsely claiming to be sympathetic to the goals of the others in the group, while intentionally working against the group by posting derailing comments and messages of 'concern' about the goals, discussion or activities of the group. They work to spread misinformation, to derail and distract the group, and to create dissent.

Know the law, know your rights
...

Cyberthreats

Columnist Van Badham told me that she gets 'a hundred threats in a good week – to my professional reputation, my personal relationships, to my body, my job, or my life.' This volume of hate dished out online is simply staggering, and all too common. Some cyberthreats, like threats of death, rape and physical violence, are also against the law. It is an offence to threaten someone with physical harm online. It is also an offence to encourage a person to kill themselves.

I recommend that any person using digital technology and online spaces familiarise themselves with the relevant laws. Australian website www.lawstuff.org.au is one helpful and freely accessible online legal resource aimed at young people. It makes the laws in relation to cyber offences quite plain: 'It is a crime to use a phone or the internet [to] threaten, harass or seriously offend somebody. A message or post could be considered offensive if it is likely to cause serious anger, outrage, humiliation or disgust. The maximum penalty is 3 years in jail.'[5]

It gives this real-life example: 'In 2010, a 20 year old guy in QLD sent threats and hate-filled texts and Facebook messages to his ex-girlfriend and her new boyfriend. He was found guilty of using phone and internet services in a menacing, harassing or offensive way and placed on probation with an order to attend counselling.' And a second example: 'In 2011, a teenager in NSW made a Facebook page called "All ___ Police

> I recommend that any person using digital technology and online spaces familiarise themselves with the relevant laws.

Are Corrupt", which included the names of several local police officers. He was charged with harassing and offensive use of the internet.'

Law Stuff also points out that 'Threatening to kill someone carries a maximum penalty of 10 years in jail' and 'It is a crime under both NSW and national law to cyber bully someone in a way that intentionally encourages or causes them to kill themselves. The maximum penalty is 5 years in jail.'[6]

There *are* cases of people being successfully prosecuted for online threats and harassment, yet most offences online still go unreported – or, if reported, don't result in fines, jail time or other penalties. At the time of writing there are moves to take legal action against online platforms that allow criminal messages and images to be posted. Be aware that these behaviours are illegal and if you participate you could find yourself with criminal charges.

Revenge porn

Many countries have specific laws against revenge porn. The Philippines introduced a specific revenge porn law as far back as 2009 and Canada, the US[7] and Japan have followed suit. The UK introduced legislation outlawing the distribution of a private sexual image of someone without their consent, as long as there's intention to 'cause distress'. Israel reportedly became the first country to classify a revenge porn perpetrator as a sex offender, in 2014. Other countries also have legislation, and efforts are being made to update laws to keep in step with technology and use. Google and Microsoft have announced they'll remove links from search results when reported by victims, and Twitter, Facebook and Reddit have banned revenge porn posts.

In Australia, revenge porn distributors can currently be charged under various laws in different States. In August 2014 the State of Victoria made it a criminal offence to maliciously distribute intimate images without the subject's consent, with up to two years' imprisonment for distributing images and up to a year for threatening to distribute images. Perpetrators can be charged with publishing 'indecent articles' for circulating intimate photographs or video without consent under the New South Wales *Crimes Act* 1900; in South Australia for the distribution of an invasive image under the *Summary Offences Act* 1953; or throughout Australia for 'using a carriage service to cause offence or to harass or menace another person' under Commonwealth telecommunications legislation.

At the time of writing there are also moves to introduce national revenge porn legislation in Australia's federal parliament. Labor MP Tim Watts – who introduced a private member's bill with colleague Terri Butler in October 2015 – said that 'Revenge porn is the most extreme example of how some men are using new technologies to exercise power and control over the women in their lives.'[8]

> ## Revenge porn is the most extreme example of how some men are using new technologies to exercise power and control over the women in their lives.
> ### TIM WATTS

Watts gave several highly disturbing examples of how women across the country have been targeted by revenge porn, which he believes should be legally regarded as sexual assault. For example, a woman in Victoria was drugged, became unconscious, and was filmed as she was sexually assaulted. She initially chose not to report the crime or seek help because of the deep shame and humiliation she felt. (Again, victims/survivors of sexual assault are made to feel they have been shamed by the crimes committed against them, though they have done nothing wrong.) Another example involved a Muslim woman who sought help from domestic violence services after photos of her in a bra and without her hijab were shared on a perpetrator's Facebook page for her children and family to see, leading to humiliation. Watts said while there was still a community attitude that led some to blame women for taking pictures of themselves in the first place, victim-blaming was wrong: 'It's the same as telling a woman who was raped that she was asking for it when she decided to wear a short skirt, or go out at night. Telling women that they should lock themselves up and cover up their bodies to avoid getting raped is wrong.'

Familiarise yourself with the law, as well as the policies and reporting protocols of the apps and online platforms you use. If you are being harassed in any way, you can take snapshots of the offending messages, including dates and times, block the user and report them to the platform or app you are using. You can also consider reporting the perpetrator to your local police or other relevant authorities. (See **What to do if it's happening to you** on pages 231 to 235.)

Online safety

...

Cyberstalking, cyberbullying, identity theft and other forms of
online harm are never the fault of the victim, no matter what you
hear. All consenting adults have the right to do what they want
online – including visiting the sites of their choice, sharing the
images and information of their choice, and engaging with others in
the ways they choose – within the common boundaries of respectful
engagement and ethics, and of the relevant laws as discussed in this
chapter.

I am often asked about online safety by my readers. Habits can
vary greatly from one person to the next, but below I have gathered
some simple, flexible steps you can consider to manage your online
privacy, exposure and safety in ways that work for you. I have used
many of these tips in my day-to-day dealings with the online world,
as well as in difficult times when harassed or stalked – which sadly
happens to too many people on the net. Overall, I find that creating
firm privacy boundaries can be helpful for your sanity in both good
and bad times.

1. Keep strong, unique passwords, change them regularly and don't share them

Secure password practices can help to prevent hacking of your
accounts, and reduce the chances of identify theft and invasion of
your privacy. Strong passwords are important for social media and
apps, but also shopping sites like Ebay and Etsy, online banking sites
and payment systems like PayPal if you use them. Do not use the
same password across accounts and avoid sharing your password
with anyone.

As a general rule, the following character sets should *all* be
included in *every* password:

Upper-case letters such as A, B, C

Lower-case letters such as a, b, c

Numerals such as 1, 2, 3

Special characters such as $, ?, &

Alt characters such as µ, £, Æ

No one is perfect, and no amount of good password practice can guarantee safety all the time, but these methods are considered by online experts to reduce risk of privacy and safety breaches.

2. If you aren't sure about an email don't click the link

A large number of email users receive multiple fraudulent emails each week, including 'phishing' emails. These emails often appear to be communications from a bank or other financial institution, usually asking the user to follow a link in order to update personal bank account details or login details – but clicking on the link may download a program that captures the user's banking login details and sends them to a third party.

Another common form of email fraud involves communications that appear to be from post offices, or for traffic fines, but that trigger 'ransomware' to be downloaded when clicked, causing the user to be locked out of their system until they pay a ransom.

If an institution ever contacts you unexpectedly by email, or an institution you expect emails from sends you something that doesn't look quite right, call the institution and ask them about it but don't click.

3. Consider the potential impacts of information, images or video before sharing

Intentionally or not, private information and images, including family photographs, images from parties, and nude or sexually explicit photographs or video, can now be circulated widely in a short period of time, thanks to the wonders of digital technology. Material may be filmed without consent, stolen from a person's home or electronic device, leaked through online security breaches of iCloud or other storage drives, or maliciously or accidentally shared by someone who was entrusted with it. For this reason, it is important to consider any unintended consequences of sharing information or images, including video, before doing so.

Ask yourself:

- If I were in this photo/video, would I be comfortable with having it seen by strangers?
- If this information was about me, would I be happy having it shared?
- Would I be breaching anyone's trust by sharing it?
- Would sharing it make public something a person has been keeping private?
- Does it contain clearly identifiable images of children, and if so, have the parents or guardians consented to the photo/video and its use online?
- Would it incriminate anyone, including me? For instance, does it show any laws being broken? underage drinking? drug-taking? assault? trespass?
- Does it contain nudity, and if so, are all the participants, including me, comfortable with sharing it?

If you have any doubts, always get clear and explicit consent from those who appear in the photo or video before posting.

Be aware that being in possession of nude or sexually explicit images of people who are underage can put a person at risk of serious child pornography offences – even if the person believes the images were filmed and circulated with the consent of the subject, or if those featured in the images are in an intimate relationship. *The Australian* this year reported on the case of a Year Six boy who coerced an 11-year-old girl in his class to text him a naked photo. He sent it to 21 mates, breaking the basics of trust and putting himself at risk of child pornography offences.[9] In recent years, the Australian Federal Police have prosecuted eight children between the ages of 10 and 17 for child pornography offences.[10]

For some consenting adults, privately sharing nude or sexually explicit images is a part of their courtship or relationship, and they have every right. Yet circulation of those images beyond their intimate partner or other mutually chosen recipients, when it does happen, constitutes a serious and painful breach of privacy and trust.

Always consider what *you* want before sharing images of yourself, particularly if you are feeling pressured for any reason. If someone shares nude or intimate images of you without consent, consider taking action against them.

4. Keep a sticker over all web cameras

In many tech offices I notice that 90% of laptops have stickers over the camera. Why? Some material circulated or posted online has been captured entirely without the knowledge or consent of the subject. Perpetrators hack web cameras, home security cameras or even wireless baby monitors, and anything you (or your children) do within view of that device is live-streamed online.

I recommend placing a sticker over any web cameras when they are not in use, including the camera built into your laptop. If you come across material online and have reason to believe the subject has not consented to the filming or distribution of their image, **do**

Viewing private material that has been produced without consent should never become acceptable.

not view it, save it, or circulate it. Viewing private material that has been produced without consent should never become acceptable.

5. Protect your personal information

The sharing of particular details and information will be acceptable for some people and not for others, depending on each person's needs. Consider your own needs when revealing your personal information, and consider the needs of others when posting information about them. If you aren't sure, always ask if it is OK to reveal a particular detail about someone online before you do so – including naming a workplace or a child, or posting identifying photographs of people or locations.

More information on your rights, including rights to your image, rights to privacy and protecting your personal information, is available at *Lawstuff*,[11] and I highly recommend that all online users read and consider it.

This advice about personal information is particularly important for activists or others who are in the public eye, for reasons that are probably already evident to you from reading other parts of this book. If you are aiming to speak out publicly, or are already doing so, I hope this information is helpful to you. We will delve a little further into 'surviving social media' next.

For more specific tips about protecting your personal information, see the box on pages 223 to 225.

> Consider your own needs when revealing your personal information, and consider the needs of others when posting information about them.

Tips for protecting your personal information

1. Check your privacy settings and respect other people's privacy

The vast majority of online posts, dating back years, can be easily tracked down and searched by anyone with the inclination, so think about what you post and how far it might reach, both in terms of your own needs and the privacy expectations of others who are mentioned in your posts. Check your privacy settings, and if you have any concerns or are unsure, avoid posting highly personal information, or information that publicly identifies your location. You can always give that information out privately rather than in public posts, if you choose.

2. Don't post your home address or phone number – or those of other people – online

If you need to have a publicly available address online, you can use a PO box or a non-residential address. This will help reduce (but not entirely remove) the chance that strangers, including doxers, will track you down at home.

If you find that your address or number has been published online without your consent, find out where (Facebook, Twitter, a chat room etc) and either contact the individual who posted it or the online platform to request that it be removed. Call your telephone provider and change your number if needed. Sites like justdelete.me also have a directory of links that allow you to remove your account from different web services that have your personal information. If you are in doubt about whether your home contact details have been published, search yourself online to see what others can find.

You are unlikely to be doxed, but it does happen. If it happens to you, get support – for example, from *Australian Cybercrime Online Reporting Network* (ACORN) (www.acorn.gov.au), or *IDCare* (www.idcare.org). *Crash Override Network* (www.crashoverridenetwork.com) is a network of former targets of online harassment, supporting others and helping with information on how to survive and prevent online harm. They have useful advice on doxing.[12]

3. Limit disclosure of your email address and mobile number

Consider limiting disclosure of your email address and mobile number, including in any surveys, app requests and more.

4. Opt out of allowing your info to be used for marketing purposes

Consider opting out of any requests for your personal information to be used for marketing purposes. There is often an 'opt out' button.

5. Consider avoiding apps and devices that track and broadcast your physical location

Personally, I advise against the regular use of mobile location and tracking devices, and apps that broadcast your physical location. As always, weigh up the pros and cons of such apps and discontinue using them if you have any concerns. Always check with others before tagging or broadcasting their whereabouts in case they have any concerns about having their location broadcast.

Tracking apps and devices are commonly used by friends to catch up, but can also be used maliciously to locate you, your home or your favourite haunts by strangers, exes or other undesirables, who may show up uninvited. These experiences are not common, but they do happen, and if you have any reason to believe you may be at risk, removing these devices and apps is a good first step, along with contacting support and local authorities if appropriate.

6. Consider avoiding free apps

Most free apps operate on a business model that involves gathering your personal data and selling it on. Such apps are commonly called 'greyware' – applications that may not have any recognisable malware concealed within them, but nevertheless are potentially harmful to a user, tracking their location and browsing habits and gathering their personal details and contacts, as well as serving up unwanted ads. As always, weigh up the pros and cons and consider what is right for you.

Managing privacy for your sanity

...

Social media is now a common forum for speaking out, and has many upsides. It is not private, however, and is therefore not a place for private discussions, private images or private spaces in your life. The following are some habits I have found helpful for managing my sense of the private and public in terms of online spaces and social media use, for my own sanity. Sometimes I need reminding, but on the whole I find these rules work for me. They may work for you too.

Keep your computer and similar devices in common areas of your house, and avoid using them in private areas.

This is better for your sleep and your sanity and for creating a necessary psychological buffer between you and things you may encounter in the larger digital world. Opening up the digital world on your device is like opening your front door and walking out into the world. You need to have a psychological buffer, and that is harder to achieve when you are vulnerable, possibly undressed and alone, and in a private, intimate space. Your bathroom or bed is not open to just anyone, so do not open yourself up to just anything when you are there. Reserve those spaces for safety and privacy, not for public life and public interactions.

> Opening up the digital world on your device is like opening your front door and walking out into the world. You need to have a psychological buffer.

If you have a child, encourage the same boundaries. Most of all, be a good digital citizen.

As a simple rule, if you wouldn't say a particular thing to someone's face, think hard about whether writing it to them online, and creating digital evidence is such good idea. Likewise, if someone is saying the sorts of things to you online that you would never stand for in the physical world, remember that you can walk away and stop listening online too, just as you would in the street – hit 'block', 'mute' or 'ban'. There is no logical need for you to be available to literally everyone in the world who has the use of a computer or similar device. (For more on this, see the next chapter, **Surviving Social Media**.)

> If someone is saying the sorts of things to you online that you would never stand for in the physical world, remember that you can walk away and stop listening online too.

CHAPTER 13

SURVIVING SOCIAL MEDIA

How to survive online

...

As I noted in the last chapter, I am often asked by readers about how I handle online interactions, and particularly trolls and abuse on social media. As so many women who 'speak out' now use online spaces as at least one of their platforms, and because online spaces are still areas of emerging technology and law, there is a lot to cover. In this chapter we will continue to explore some responses to online experiences from myself and other women, and we will also take a closer look at what you might like to do in the event that you are faced with abuse when speaking out on social media platforms.

There is no right response for every person and situation, so we are unlikely to always get it 'right' (whatever that means), and I certainly can't advise you on how to get it right each time. I can only share what works for me, and what other women have experienced. The focus should always be on your safety and wellbeing.

And remember, you don't have to do this alone.

> There is no right response for every person and situation, so we are unlikely to always get it 'right' (whatever that means).

What to do if it's happening to you ...

If you are being abused – online *or* in the physical world – the first thing to be clear on is that *the abuse is the fault of the perpetrator*. It is *not* your fault. Anyone who suggests otherwise is either misinformed, or part of the problem.

When a perpetrator is committing a harmful act against someone, that behaviour is always wrong. Unfortunately, widespread victim-blaming means that many people will focus disproportionately on the response of those being victimised – why they did or did not respond, why they 'put themselves out there' in the first place, why they posted what they did, or consented to being photographed, why they don't just turn off their computer, cease to exist etc – instead of focusing on the perpetrator and their choices. I have mentioned this elsewhere in this book, but it bears repeating.

> The first thing to be clear on is that *the abuse is the fault of the perpetrator.*

There is no wrong way to respond to abuse (with the exception of committing a crime), as long as *you* are coping. Only you can fully understand what your situation is, what your needs are, and how safe you feel. You need to do what you have to for *you*.

Tips for dealing with online abuse

Here are some widely acknowledged tips for dealing with online abuse. They will not work for everyone in every circumstance, but I use many of them myself, and I share them here in the hope that some of you will find these tips helpful.

1. Collect evidence

Most experts and online users agree that reporting online abuse is important, particularly when threats of any kind are involved. To report any abusive material or to lodge any complaints against a perpetrator, you'll need evidence. Take a screen shot and copy the URL of any abusive material that concerns you. Store the evidence in a folder on your computer so you can retrieve it in future if needed. By taking notes and collecting evidence, you will also be able to confirm if it is the same person or people who are routinely abusing you.

While I don't record all abuse I receive online by any means, I do have a folder for such unpleasant things, and it has come in handy from time to time. If you are threatened with violence, or you recognise the person sending you abusive messages as someone you know, or someone who is routinely abusing, harassing or stalking you, be sure to collect evidence and report them.

> To report any abusive material or to lodge any complaints against a perpetrator, you'll need evidence.

2. Report the offending content to the social media service

Even before you are sent any threatening or abusive material on a social media service, you should try to familiarise yourself with the policies of that service. This means that if it happens (which is unfortunately very common), you'll already know your options for reporting the material. Collecting evidence, as suggested in tip 1 above, will make the process easier. By familiarising yourself with policies you can also make more informed decisions about what social media platforms you want to use.

In 2015, Australia's eSafety Commissioner announced new partnerships with several social media companies, which agreed to take down offensive material within 12 hours if requested to do so. Four other companies – Google Plus, Facebook, Instagram and YouTube – are now legally bound to take bullying material down within two days if requested. Be confident about your right to report abuse. It might not always be easy or even possible, but the more we do report serious abuse, the more likely we are to achieve a safer online experience for everyone.

3. Consider reporting the offending content to the police, particularly if it involves personal threats, privacy breaches or other crimes

Only you can decide whether to report online abuse to the police. Know that it is within your rights to do so. Again, you will need to have collected evidence of the abuse and/or online crimes in order to report it. I take death threats and threats of physical violence very seriously and I report them.

4. Block early, block often

If someone is abusive to me, I block them so they can't go on reaching me with their abuse. Occasionally that person goes out of their way to find other ways to reach me, often attempting to abuse me further via other people, or by using other accounts to spread the word that I banned them and this is a 'restriction of their freedom of speech'.

Let's be clear: it is *not* a restriction of free speech to ban an abusive person on the internet.

Let's be clear: it is *not* a restriction of free speech to ban an abusive person on the internet any more than it is a restriction of free speech to walk away from someone who is abusing you on the street. In short, they can say what they want where they want, but I won't be listening or responding. That is how blocking works.

As I have already mentioned, some cyber abuse is also a crime. Blocking or banning is never a crime. It is the only way online platforms can function, considering that there are (unfortunately) a percentage of people who are abusive. They are a small minority, but there are enough of them to often make online spaces either unpleasant or unsafe for the rest of us.

If someone is abusive to *others* and I witness that, I also tend to block them, and depending on the severity of the abuse I may even report them. Sometimes, when I see other women or men being trolled I will go to the page/feed of the troller, have a quick sweep of their posts, find that they are one of those predictable types who troll people all day, block them and carry on. Often the feeds are quite revealing in that respect.

By pre-emptively blocking, there's one troll whose hateful opinions I won't need to be subjected to. And if an account gets blocked by a huge number of people, some sites will notice that and may deal with complaints about that person differently.

> If you're a user of online spaces there is no requirement that you give time to any particular person. Abusive people don't deserve to reach you.

As writer and film-maker Ruby Hamad says: 'Block early. Block often.'[1] If you're a user of online spaces there is no requirement that you give time to any particular person. Abusive people don't deserve to reach you. Block and ban at will.

5. Consider the advice to 'think twice'

When it comes to trolls, the most common advice from e-safety advocates is not to engage, and that advice is good. Over the years I have come to use the 'ban' and 'block' buttons more and more freely. I have also found that my days tend to be more pleasant when I don't engage in back-and-forths with hostile types or dedicated time-wasters I will never meet and who otherwise have no bearing on my life.

So why do I write 'think twice' before engaging rather than simply saying 'don't engage'?

Because a) I don't know you or your specific situation and b) *you are the priority here*, so you should do what you need to for you – whether that means taking a snapshot for evidence and reporting the abuser, or responding (see pages 236 to 239 for tips), or simply hitting the 'block' or 'ban' button, or ignoring the comment altogether.

It's widely reported that not responding directly to online attacks can reduce the number of attacks you personally receive. But there are many exceptions to this rule, unfortunately. Engaging with attackers can have the effect of making them reconsider their actions, but it can also have the effect of encouraging them, depending on the individual you are dealing with. Some will seek you out no matter how diligently you ignore them. You can't always predict how people you know will respond, let alone those you've never met.

If you feel you want to respond to online attacks, you have every right to do so. Sometimes when I respond I feel better. Only *you* know your personal situation, and only you can assess what you want to do on an individual basis, as no two online interactions are the same. (Well, some sure seem like it, but you know what I mean.) It is my experience that engagement often leads to more engagement, so I tend to choose those I engage with carefully. I can't always anticipate what will happen next, naturally, but my interaction with the world involves not being silenced (hence this book), and that goes for online as well as offline spaces.

If someone responds to a troll or highlights the abuse they are getting, support them. The abuse is wrong. Not the response.

If you respond, how should you respond?

...

If someone is rude or threatening I generally do not respond, but there may be occasions when it suits me to reply and acknowledge what they have written. This goes for abusive trolls as well as the subtler 'concern trolls', or dedicated time-wasters, who have a kind of veiled hostility that isn't glaringly obvious in a first post. Generally, when I do choose to respond I do it in one of the following ways.

1. Stat them

Even when a poster is hostile, or I can tell they're not really interested in knowing the facts or having their mind changed, I may choose to thank them for their query and post a series of links to statistics and further information on the subject – from the United Nations, the World Health Organization, the Australian Bureau of Statistics, the Fair Work Commission, the Workplace Gender Equality Agency and so on.

Once you have got used to doing this it will take only a few minutes each time, and will serve to further sharpen your own knowledge and views on the given subject. It also often helps others viewing these public exchanges to find links to further reading.

If, as is often the case, the poster responds, having clearly not read the info and without providing any links to data of their own, you can again direct them to your links.

This method is clean, sharp and professional, and yes, you will likely want to ignore, or if needed, block them, after your initial response with links and a second response to again suggest they read them. Anything beyond that tends to be well and truly time-wasting in my experience, unless you sense that a truly constructive exchange is taking place (it does happen from time to time). Given the space to, some will fill my social media page or feed with comment after comment, post after post, in a seemingly never-ending demand for further reply once I have offered one or two comments in direct response to their queries. I have often had other followers on social media comment that 'I am a very patient woman' when dealing with this sort of thing. I have limits, of course, and so does my time. And your time should, too. As a rule, two or three replies is generally my cut off unless I am really looking at a mutually constructive exchange.

2. Respond with humour

I have, at times, had some success with using humour. I recall a particular day when I'd appeared on TV and among the online messages of support and questions, there was a tweet that said something like, '@tara_moss You look like a man.' I responded with 'Pregnant dudes are awesome!' (I was pregnant at the time.) This particular person replied, somewhat embarrassed, and thanked me for taking it so well and being so good natured. I did not hear from him again.

I can't say that response would work as well with everyone, but sometimes you are online and you just want to respond *for you*. Little gems can sometimes result.

Comedian John Cleese is among those who likes to occasionally re-tweet a nasty comment he receives, with a humorous reply. After mentioning his wife in a tweet, using her name, someone snarkily replied, 'Have you got through so many you have to refer to your wives by their full name?', to which Cleese answered, 'Would you prefer that I referred to my wife as Mrs John Cleese ? I thought this was considered a little out-dated ...'[2] John hardly has all day to respond to random people online, let alone the ones who are rude, but there is a reason many of us do it from time to time – for *us*.

Former *Star Trek* actor and gay rights activist George Takei has over 9 million followers on Facebook, and posted one of his humorous responses to a trolling comment that said 'George Takei you SUCK'. 'And well, I'm told', he responded. He took a snapshot of the public exchange and posted it on Facebook with the words, 'Sorry, couldn't help myself. #Trollololollol.'[3] At the time of writing it has been liked by nearly half a million people. (Be aware that posting snapshots of exchanges publicly without blacking out the name of the poster can, rightly or wrongly, sometimes result in complaints or temporary bans, depending on the social media platform, believe it or not. This even happened to me once, after posting a snapshot of a pretty mild exchange.)

At a talk at the University of Sydney in 2015, George reiterated his belief that humour has worked for him not only in dealing with trolls, but also in making his time online more enjoyable and helping him reach a wider audience with his messages. With a grin, he said his number one 'pro-tip' for handling online trolls is 'Grumpy cat'.

Humour doesn't work for everyone, and doesn't suit everyone's personality or field of work, but some find it very effective. I lack John's comic genius and George's pun-abilities, but I can still enjoy the odd humorous exchange with a person I might have otherwise ignored.

3. Kill them with kindness

I always recommend this general approach for anyone who feels compelled to respond to someone questionable online. By being polite and kind, you can kind of 'float above' the more objectionable elements of what they write. It can sometimes be enough simply to respond to a horrid comment with 'Thank you. I wish you a wonderful day and success in all your endeavours.' They are unlikely to expect it, your polite response will tend to put their rudeness in stark relief, and perhaps you'll feel relieved of your initial frustration with the troll, and you can then move on.

I tend to think about how I am feeling and whether I want to go there, knowing it could end up resulting in further engagement. But yeah, if I want to I'll go there, and you can too. It's your life and your online account. Use it as you see fit.

4. Out them

If someone is abusive or threatening to me or others, I report them (see pages 232 to 233). Retweeting, or 'publicly calling out', can also be an option for some, but is more complicated. You can end up with a stream of messages attacking or defending the abuser, filling your feed for hours or days. And because it is the internet, even if you have a small following it is possible for anyone to retweet these messages and it can become a far larger or more sustained experience than you might have initially imagined. Put simply, this technique is important for public awareness, but is not for everyone.

Early on in my use of social media, I did on occasion retweet messages when doing so made a point about the types of attitudes women are up against. As my online following has grown, however, I find I do this with a smaller percentage of the abuse I receive, for practical reasons. I more frequently screen-capture messages and collect them, then republish them with the user names blurred or removed, and use the messages themselves to demonstrate particular attitudes, forms of abuse and so on.

While reporting online abuse to the social media platform, and if necessary to the police, is directed at an individual and at stopping that individual from continuing their behaviour, public outing of this kind is more about the messages and patterns of abuse, which arguably protects the sender (who may be underage) and also protects me. This is a personal choice I have made over time, but it won't be right for everyone. I assess each situation individually. Most of the time, I simply click 'block' and move on from the rudeness, or report them if their message is abusive or threatening.

A final note

...

Dear trolls,

I've been using social media for some years now, and I get a lot out of it. I like hearing from readers and other writers. I enjoy hearing about other people's experiences, and I learn from it. I find the vast majority of discussions positive and interesting, even where there is disagreement.

But there are other kinds of engagements, of course, and they usually take on the same tiresome patterns. This is why many social media users like the 'block' and 'ban' buttons. It tends to keep the virtual air a whole lot cleaner.

With that in mind, here are five quick pointers for you dedicated social media users the rest of us know as 'trolls', who when blocked by sensible people, enjoy complaining bitterly about how others refuse to 'debate' them:

1. If you genuinely want debate, try using facts. It's more engaging. By this I don't mean to suggest that every assertion out there is easy to fact-check, but if you are already on the internet there are simple means of checking the essentials. For instance, read a person's bio or look them up before making obviously false claims about them. In short, even if there is disagreement, people are more likely to engage in debate with you if you make some attempt at being informed.

2. Ask yourself: 'Am I insulting someone based on their appearance? their race? their gender or sexual orientation?' If you answered 'yes' to any of these, this may be why people are not interested in your idea of 'debate'.

3. Ask yourself: 'Am I threatening someone with physical injury? Am I threatening sexual or other kinds of violence? Am I encouraging someone to kill themselves?' If the answer to any of these is 'yes', know that these actions are just as illegal online or in the mail as they are in person. This is not 'debate'. This is not 'freedom of speech'. Stop doing it.

4. I block early, and I block often. So do many others. It isn't actually an infringement of your freedom of speech to no longer be able to spew directly at me from your keyboard, but if it helps, you can imagine me lighting a candle to mourn the abusive conversations I'll never get to have because you, a total stranger, wrote something rude you'd never dream of saying to someone's face, and I clicked 'block' or 'ban' – or perhaps even 'report'.

5. Life is genuinely more rewarding when we engage respectfully. No one is perfect, but we can at least be civil.

Tara

P.S. I do hate the term 'troll'. Can we get a new one? Trolls are mythical creatures. People who misuse the internet are not.

CHAPTER 14

STORIES OF SURVIVAL

Tips from women who have been there

...

While I have included a lot of information on surviving online and in public life, different women use different strategies. I hope the real-life examples below, as told to me, will show you that women of different backgrounds and different circumstances receive abuse, and that different choices work for different women.

Van Badham, columnist, author, playwright

'I found myself targeted for abuse from the moment I started tweeting on political subjects and when I was employed to write my column for *The Guardian*, it intensified. In the beginning I treated it as a word-game – the nastiness were just words on a screen, after all – and I engaged and responded with repartee in the way that I would if heckled at a stand up comedy gig ... The abuse [ended up being] much darker than I realised ... the real-world physical threats and the stalking that resulted from what was happening online took me completely by surprise. When the first threat turned up it took me a whole hour to call the police because I just couldn't believe these people were really out there.'

Why did the barrage of harassment and threats come once Van was speaking out on political topics?

'The issue is, of course, that social institutions were once male preserves, and the discussion of politics, economy and society was one made by men to men,' Van says.

'Feminism has shattered this paradigm by legislating opportunities for women to participate in education, institutions and employment on an equal basis, and social media has also allowed women to engage in public conversation at their own instigation, rather than at institutional generosity ... The minority of men whose sense of self is based on myths of male superiority are terrified by women like me; we're avatars of a new world in which they can no longer assume dominance over 51% of the population merely by virtue of waking up in the morning. Their fear manifests in hateful abuse … It reverts to name-calling, harassment, threats of violence, attempts at sexual violence and, at its worst, physical threat.

'Now, I block. I block without hesitation.'

Rosie Batty, domestic violence campaigner and Australian of the Year 2015

In 2014, Rosie's son, Luke, 11, was murdered at cricket practice by his estranged father, Greg Anderson, in front of shocked onlookers. Greg had a history of domestic abuse, had several criminal charges against him and was the subject of four arrest warrants due to breach of bail conditions and failure to attend court. He was shot by officers at the scene when he lunged at them. During the hearing into the case, Senior Constable Topham told the court, 'I was astounded that he still got bail based on the information that we had.'[1]

Despite the fact that Rosie had done everything in her power to protect her son from his father, after Luke's death she received some of the most vicious victim-blaming hate mail and messages I have personally seen. Some members of the public – a minority, but nonetheless a vocal one – blamed the bereaved mother for her ex-partner's deadly violence. 'For me, I think it's the victim-blaming that hurts the most,' Rosie explains.

Every person can be subjected to abuse online or in other ways by members of the public, but when it relates to the tragic death of your own child, it can also be triggering. As mentioned previously, Rosie took the step of largely retreating from social media and not reading comments about her and her murdered son. But by focusing her efforts on working with experts to prevent violence against women and children, and not on negative commentary by uninformed strangers, Rosie has become a powerful advocate and agent for change.

'I became quickly linked with some very trustworthy, supportive people who were my mentors,' she explains. 'They had the expertise and could support me with my messaging. I knew they always had my best interests at heart. I built a small network of people I could trust, with the professional information I needed [relating to domestic violence and family violence rates, statistics, programs and available services], but the emotional support as well. I don't think I would have been as confident, and I don't think I would have been able to be as informed without that support. To continue, I need to have that around me. I've always chosen to work inclusively and collaboratively.'

Carly Findlay, blogger and appearance activist

'I speak up about ableism, othering [to view or treat a person or group as intrinsically different from and alien to oneself] and discrimination,' Carly says. 'I organised Australia's first ichthyosis meet in 2014 – bringing together 75 people from Australia and New Zealand, fundraising and working with the venue, medical professionals and sponsors.' Ichthyosis is a rare, severe genetic skin condition, and something Carly suffers from. 'I had a little help, but it was mostly done on my own. It was an amazing day and I was very proud. For many attendees, it was the first time they'd met someone else with the skin condition.'

Unfortunately, being an organiser sometimes means getting negative feedback, even if you are doing it on your own, unpaid. As Carly explains, 'A few people told me I excluded them because they didn't know about the meet, and I was accused of being too proud. Despite the enormous positive feedback, I was devastated at the nasty stuff said.'

One of the biggest challenges was when her image was appropriated online. 'In December 2013 my photo was misused on Reddit.[2] I woke up to thousands of hits on my blog, because someone had shared my photo on the "What the F*ck?" forum, ridiculing it. People asked what my vagina looked like, told me I looked like something their dog vomited and said I should be killed with fire. I could have curled up in a ball and cried, but I responded to the hate, calmly and articulately. I linked to my blog so people could see the real me.

'Within minutes, I had turned that hateful thread around. People defended me, got to know me, apologised even. After writing about it on my blog, I made Australian and international news.

'I fought back with awesome after one of my worst fears came true. It helped to have amazing support around me. This hate speech is so damaging – especially to those without immediate support.'

Carly continues: 'I've made sure I talk to people who understand online writing when I am feeling a bit down or on the receiving end of nasty comments. Writer friends have been invaluable for advice and support. Sure I can tell my mum and get a hug, but she'll tell me to switch off the computer, and it's not that easy.'

What does Carly do to negotiate her self-care in the face of hate speech and other challenges she comes up against?

'I take time out. I couldn't write about appearance diversity and disability issues all the time – I'd burn out and also seem constantly angry to my readers – which I am not. So at times, I don't blog, and I don't apologise for it.'

Amy Gray, writer

Amy is a writer for publications such as *The Guardian* and *The Age*. She writes on tech, politics and gender issues and can get hundreds of comments on her pieces in a given day, many of them vitriolic. 'Writing opinion editorial as a vaguely public woman can be tiring in the face of a system that will exert enormous energy in an effort to try to silence and discredit you,' she explains. 'It's not necessarily the writing that is draining, it's just the expectation you will be instantly available to wear people's tired rhetoric and anger.

'When that gets too much, you need to find something that will fill up what's been taken. Now, this is where I would differ from most because I think filling up isn't about short pleasures, I think it's about action. So that could be exploring an issue that's blown up and seeing what you can do that will create lasting change or striking back somehow. That really fills you up and helps you cope because you can see that you can change things, you can help others and yourself. That's how I've ended up on advisory boards, emailed newspaper editors to discuss how they report on violence against women, removed sponsors from offensive events or connected with damn smart people. You learn to cope by seeing the change you make.'

'But we can't always do that,' Amy concedes. 'If I'm feeling more introverted and unable to work or fill myself up, though, I normally escape into music or film for a few hours and take the day off … The other thing you should always remember is that you can control your environment. Twitter mentions blowing up? Switch it to mentions from only people you follow. Still not working? Delete that f**ker and every other social media foghorn off your phone and block it momentarily from your computer. Someone's being annoying? Block them. Don't want to deal with blog noise? Turn off comments. No one is paying you to be abused and they aren't entitled to your time … I'm pretty strategic about my work. I know that I will get far more blowback from work published online than printed. Sometimes I just focus on getting published in print instead of digital publications if it all gets too much. However, there's a natural tension there because your work will always get more widely-read and discussed if you get published online so you need to balance your need to work with your need to give yourself space from abuse.'

Amanda Palmer, artist, rock star, crowd-funding pioneer

'I've been through so many internet controversies, and the biggest thing I've learned is that there's always some hidden flower that grows out of the dung-heap. [For example] my kickstarter controversy led to my TED talk, which led to my book [*The Art Of Asking*] ... Things happen, things suck, and then other things happen in the sand left behind in the waves of those awful moments ... you just need to be looking and open. I have a real philosophical policy of no regrets, and I struggle with it all the time.'

Amanda is very public about trolls and negative comments about her. 'One thing I try to do is to air out all the troll-garbage publicly,' she says. 'There's a real art to doing this, and social media is so tricky. But usually just pointing to negative things and saying: "wow, this person said something awful about me and it's making me depressed and kinda insecure" can feel empowering. It also humanises you: whoever the critic or troll is has to confront the fact that they've hurt a fellow human being. And it feels a lot more honest than saying "LA LA LA YOU CAN'T HURT ME!!", because often that's just bullsh*t. Things do hurt, and you can acknowledge that hurt without giving it too much mind or power. It's also important not to use your reach, power, or influence to keep the cycle of nastiness going. Acceptable is: "I feel this. This felt sh*tty. Reading this feels devastating." Unacceptable is: "Look at what this a**hole wrote about me. Everybody tell them to f*ck off." Public life means that you have power, and if you want good karma, you have to make sure you never use your power to hurt. I used to have an entire section of my website dedicated to the "hate mail" my band got. It was one of the most popular pages. And I loved it.'

Karen Pickering, feminist organiser and educator

Karen says, 'I used to write op ed [opinion pieces] and I actually stopped because it was so taxing. Filing a story within hours of a pitch being accepted, and then spending days dealing with the fallout of sexist abuse was simply not worth the $100 pay cheque and sense of civic participation.' (See **Will you be paid?** on pages 159 to 161 for more on this issue.)

'I concentrate on other ways of organising feminists and reaching my community now, like events and online networks, as well as presenting workshops and speaking engagements. I'm also working on two books, which is an immense privilege, and a kind of writing that makes you a smaller target for harassment and abuse. I just had to find other ways of doing the same job, which is always: reach people, communicate and converse with them, help create spaces for reflection and change, and in my case, bring people into the cause of feminism or help them feel positive and hopeful within it.'

Karen acknowledges, 'All types of activism can be emotionally draining and the demands of public feminism can be particularly exhausting. The single biggest factor in my ability to cope is other women, without doubt. Other women are endlessly inspirational to me. Remembering I'm in a community with other strong, powerful, empathetic and supportive women is sometimes enough to pull me through a difficult time, but I've also learned to ask for help. It's a movement of many so it's fine to take a day off, seek solace, find out who can talk you through something or just hang out.'

Natasha Stott Despoja, AM, Australian Ambassador for Women and Girls, Chair of Our Watch and former leader of the Australian Democrats

'I believe that elected representatives and public figures should be multi-faceted: I don't have a problem with seeing different dimensions of a person's life. I think reflections on their family, or other interests, are not bad things when we look at and understand the people who reflect and represent our interests. I find, however, that politics encourages a homogenised version of a female politician. Female MPs often fear doing something different or challenging the norm, be it with appearance or lifestyle or political viewpoint, lest they suffer media and political retaliation. Women have learnt to be wary of standing out too much.'

'Visceral criticism is nothing new,' Natasha explains, 'especially of women in high profile roles, and I am not sure if the criticism is worse but the anonymity of social media commentary when directed at women in violent and sexist ways can still shock me – and I thought nothing could these days! – I feel for some of the high-profile women in parliamentary life who withstand such onslaughts on a daily basis and then, 'twas ever thus, we're always told 'to get over it' or 'not take things so seriously' or 'to move on'.

Like a lot of prominent women speaking out against violence against women, she gets violent personal threats. 'I do get threats and criticisms including violent criticisms from men around the world. The volume of it doesn't surprise me and I am buoyed occasionally by the fact that the mainstream population seems to be increasing its understanding about the nature of causes of men's violence against women so we are having an impact.'

Support networks are key. 'I have always found support networks to be crucial for women in any sphere, especially this one. I try and provide support to other women wherever I can which gives me faith that the movements keep on going and progressing. This is one way of finding some sustenance. But I do not underestimate the importance of good mental, emotional and physical health. I guess there is so much to do that I fear taking any time out from the work ahead but I am also convinced that women can share this load, we've been at this for many decades without a rest.'

Miranda Tapsell, actor

'I decided to speak out about the experiences of Indigenous Australians and women of colour because I don't believe it to be an even playing ground in terms of how much of a voice women from minority groups have in the media. I know that my great-grandmother, my grandmother and my mother weren't given that opportunity and made it so that I could. It would be remiss of me to not take it.'

For Miranda, speaking out brought a lot of attention, much of it positive, but also some of it critical, including racist comments. 'There were varied responses particularly to whether I identified myself as "an Australian". I tended to focus on the people that responded positively.' As for the rest? 'I muted or blocked the negative people and chose not to read it. Being an actor and experiencing what it's like to change negative perceptions towards a person of colour because of the roles I've played has been so exciting. I want to continue playing roles that challenge tired stereotypes and show young women from many different backgrounds what they can become.'

Saba Vasefi, Iranian political refugee, feminist film-maker

'I think I was 12 years when for the first time, by shaving my hair, I stood up to my society and the ways that it manipulated me and my body. From the age of seven, Iranian girls have to wear a hijab to go to school, and in my town, from the age of 12, as well as the hijab we had to wear the Chador. So when the time came for me to wear the Chador, I shaved my head and said to my teachers, "I have no hair to hide, so why should I wear a Chador?" They suspended me from school until my mother, who was also a school teacher, assured them her daughter would wear the Chador.'

Many years passed and Saba became a lecturer at the prestigious Shahid Beheshti University in Iran, but after four years was banned from teaching due to her activism against capital punishment. Eventually she ended up having to flee Iran with her young daughter as a political refugee. Saba's experiences and studies 'opened her eyes'. 'I saw how rebellious women were marginalised and stigmatised by dominant cultures,' she says. 'Women like Tahereh Ghoratolein, an Iranian poet, who left her conservative and religious family in Iran to join the Baha'i faith, and appeared in society unveiled. For this offence she was buried alive. I saw how in Iran, and later when I fled and settled in Australia, neither I nor any woman could escape the hypocrisy of the dominant culture ... Power only works when citizens submit to it; a culture only has the power we concede. So I learned that overt protest was not always the best way to resist the power of the state, to expose hypocrisy and make change. Sometimes the long way round is the shortest way home. In Iran, the issue for women and all free-thinking people is the lack of almost any freedom of action, speech, and choice. In Australia, I discovered, although there were more freedoms – of speech and protest and employment and belief – the dominant culture marginalised minorities, including especially immigrant groups and women, by discriminating, sometimes consciously, between racial groups, when it came to access to power and resources.'

Now Saba is a powerful agent for change in Australia. 'My studies and my own activism showed me that major social change can be wrought by resistance. Sometimes soft resistance, through storytelling; sometimes hard resistance, like protest. Always doing what you can. Never giving up. Whenever I face, or observe other women facing bullying (online or in the physical world), I realise it is just a modern manifestation of historical abuse.'

Mariam Veiszadeh, lawyer and writer

'For too long, Australian Muslim women were the topic of political controversy – much was said about them but we rarely heard from them,' says Mariam. 'The one-dimensional voiceless image of the typical Muslim woman portrayed by mainstream media didn't represent me or anyone I knew for that matter ... Social media offered me an opportunity to speak directly to the masses, bypassing the media and any potential sensationalising or editorialising of my views.

'Speaking out as an Australian Muslim woman does come with a high personal cost however,' Mariam told me. This has included sustained cyberbullying campaigns against her, and even suspicious packages being sent to her home, including one that prompted the bomb squad to come.

'The death threats in the virtual world meant that I had to worry about my safety in the real one ... I know that I am stronger than the sum of all of the hate directed at me. I know this because I am my mother's daughter – resilient, tenacious and strong. I am also human, vulnerable, sensitive and not immune to the physiological effects and mental strain that cyber-bullying has placed on me.'

She wrote this in November 2015, after a sustained bullying campaign against her that included the publication of an article by a US-based Neo-Nazi and White Supremacist group, 'falsely claiming that I got a woman "arrested" for "hurting my feelings" and openly urged their alleged "5000+" ... followers to "flood" my Twitter account with as "much racial and religious abuse as they possibly can".[3]

'The months of cyber bullying that I endured [were] incredibly harrowing – the impact extending to my family, friends and my work,' she says. 'I suffered from prolonged anxiety that manifested itself in several physical illnesses that lasted approximately six weeks. It had a disabling effect on my life. To this day, I still suffer from periods of anxiety.'

How does she go on? What helps her to get through? 'Breaks from social media and counselling help get me through it. I block, report, ignore and where I think it's appropriate, call it out.'

Karen Willis, Executive Officer of Rape & Domestic Violence Services Australia

'With social media I don't engage personally,' Karen explains. 'Email keeps me busy enough. We have started on Twitter this year (2015) and will be launching a Full Stop Facebook page that others cannot post to this week. [The Full Stop Foundation is the foundation set up by Rape & Domestic Violence Services Australia, which I launched for them in 2015, and remain patron of. The Facebook page launched in Dec 2015.] A number of other services have had their Facebook pages badly trolled and we want to avoid that.'

In terms of emails sent to Rape & Domestic Violence Services, she says, 'My first line of defence is "delete". It doesn't get to me much. It's different for people who have experienced violence and who are then attacked in this way, as it is very personal and targets the impacts of trauma they are already experiencing. For me, I know those idiots are out there ... there is a good chance they are themselves offenders, but their views and words are not personal, just to the ideas I am promoting.'

There are times when reporting these offenders is important. 'There are a couple we have reported to police. For example, when the emails or phone calls are constant and continue over a period of time, or when they indicate they have [planned] or are planning an act of violence. A visit by police explaining that their behaviour is unacceptable usually results in silence. For the second lot [those indicating they are planning violence], this info adds to police intelligence, and there have been a couple where an arrest has been made – not solely because of our info but we have assisted.'

Discover what works for you

...

No two women are the same, nor will they face precisely the same circumstances, or want to respond in precisely the same way, but by retelling triumphs and failures, and the responses we got along the way, we get a greater sense of strength. By comparing notes, we learn to recognise and differentiate constructive criticism from the diversions, the silencing and the trolling, and most importantly of all know we are human and in this together.

Thank you to each of the women who agreed to share their story of survival.

Get support and don't be afraid to report abuse

•••

Every person speaking out has to find their own strategies for coping, their own methods for dealing with online and offline abuse, and their own ways of feeling safe in the world, for the circumstances they find themselves in. There is no single 'correct' answer for everyone.

Knowing your rights, knowing you can delete, block, ban and report abuse, finding support networks, and doing what you personally need to continue speaking out are keys to many women's survival in public spaces and online. I hope some of these strategies work for you so you can speak out and continue to speak out.

Online resources for reporting abuse or getting support:

www.acorn.gov.au
(Australian Cybercrime Online Reporting Network)

www.beyondblue.org.au (mental health support)

www.eheadspace.org.au (free online and telephone mental health support for Australians aged 12 to 25)

1800 RESPECT and www.1800respect.org.au
(for those who are experiencing sexual or domestic violence which can also involve online abuse and harassment, and for those wanting to support people who are experiencing such violence)

CHAPTER 15

SELF-CARE

If you can't breathe, you can't help anyone else

...

Have you flown in a plane recently and noticed the card instructing you, in case of emergency, to 'Put on your own oxygen mask before helping those around you'? Why do they instruct passengers to do that?

Because if you can't breathe, you can't help anyone else. If you don't look after your own mental, physical and emotional wellbeing, you will eventually burn out. And we don't want that to happen, because whether you are a student, a stay-at-home mum, a shopkeeper, CEO, lawyer or activist, we need more women and girls speaking out and having their voices heard. We can't afford to lose you.

If you can't breathe, you can't help anyone else. Make sure *you* are OK too. Make sure you can breathe.

Caring for others is an excellent skill that we could see far more of in the world. Ultimately, however, it must also be balanced with self-care, or those who care for others will not be able to keep doing what they are doing.

Self-care is not something we should feel guilty about, and it is not an exercise in 'either/or' – looking after others *or* yourself. If you do not practise self-care, however, in time you may be unable to care for *anyone*, including yourself. Just as you know you must eat to survive, and sleep to survive, it is important to realise that you must also look after yourself in other ways to survive, and this mental maintenance must be part of your regular routine.

Self-care is something that may be put to the test in more difficult times of high stress or high

> Self-care is not something we should feel guilty about, and it is not an exercise in 'either/or' - looking after others *or* yourself.

workload. And though good self-care habits like sleep, hydration and mental relaxation are often the first things that go out the window at such times, it is then that we need them the most. Giving up on looking after you when things get hard is the last thing you should do.

Though this is the final chapter of this handbook, it is one of the most important. Nothing outlined in the previous chapters can be done consistently without something called 'self-care'. In fact, over time, little in life can be done, enjoyed or survived consistently without it.

Self-care is important for everyone, but in my experience it can be especially vital for women and girls who have traditionally been taught to look after and care for others but may not have spent as much time, on a regular basis, looking after themselves. This is particularly the case if they are parents or carers. Impossible standards of care and responsibility for others, without the balance of self-care, can lead to burnout, which in turn sees many women drop out of the workforce or other public endeavours, sometimes permanently. This is, in my view, one of the many factors influencing women's lower levels of participation in public life. Stress is another one. In the US, for example, women report higher rates of stress than men, and people of colour report higher rates of stress than those who are white. There are many factors involved in that stress, including sexism, racism, discrimination and financial insecurity. Women in the US earn on average 79 cents[1] for every dollar men make, and this pay gap is even wider for women of colour[2]. In Australia, women working full time earn on average 18% less than their male counterparts.

These factors make speaking out even more important, and simultaneously more difficult, making self-care even more vital.

Depression and anxiety

Women are more likely than men to experience depression (one in five women and one in eight men) and anxiety (one in three women and one in five men) over their lifetime, and although men are considerably more likely to take their own lives, women attempt suicide and self-harm at an even higher rate than men.

Georgie Harman, CEO of *beyondblue*, an Australian initiative to tackle depression and anxiety and prevent suicide, told me, 'Good mental health is essential to every one of us, but women experience depression, anxiety and post-traumatic stress at higher rates than men.' *beyondblue* list risk factors leading to stress, depression and anxiety in women as including caring for family members who are unable to look after themselves, such as children or those with a disability (women are significantly more likely to be primary carers), experiences of violence or abuse, eating disorders, same-sex attraction (with lesbian and bisexual women experiencing higher rates of stress than heterosexual women) as well as pregnancy, early motherhood and menopause.

'Research shows that over a third of carers experience severe depression and that being a carer for someone else could be one of the leading causes of their depression,' Georgie Harman explains. 'We're no good to anyone else if we don't place a premium on the health of our own minds and bodies. These facts make it even more important that as women we (literally and figuratively) "give ourselves a break", look after ourselves first, and draw support, knowledge and wisdom from others.'

Women and girls have worth independent of their roles as carers, mothers, partners, wives, girlfriends, sisters or daughters. Sometimes we need reminding of this, and a reminder that our health and wellbeing also matter.

Good self-care habits

Anyone who for whatever reason has never been shown the basic steps to achieving good mental and physical health can be transformed by good self-care habits. In time, these habits can make them healthier, better rested, and therefore more stable and productive creatively and intellectually in whatever endeavour they are pursuing – whether that is rising to the challenges of work commitments, coping with the rigours of being a parent or carer, or just *living*, and doing it better.

The activities involved in self-care will vary from person to person – as I will soon explain – and so will other factors like the amount of time taken and the amount of money (if any) spent. The only key factor is the concept of 'looking after myself, *for myself*'. This is very different from the version of 'caring for yourself' that is widely encouraged among women in mainstream Western culture. This other version focuses on watching your weight and looking after your appearance, usually with the help of commercial products or gym/diet programs, for the purpose of 'keeping yourself nice'. This may intersect with health benefits, or even improvements in other areas like self-esteem, but the focus is different, and for this reason we need to separate beauty maintenance and the like from *self-care*, even where there is a crossover.

For many women, self-care will require a rethink.

Caring for myself is not self-indulgence, it is self-preservation, and that is an act of political warfare.[3]

AUDRE LORDE

What is self-care?

...

Put simply, self-care is looking after yourself as a form of regular maintenance so that you can function in your daily life.

Self-care is consciously self-initiated and maintained. It involves acknowledging your own physical, mental and emotional needs, and taking action to maintain those vital areas of your health so you can better look after yourself and others, and avoid burnout, breakdown and vicarious trauma (see **Chapter 11**). While it involves things like eating well and getting enough exercise and rest, it also involves a great deal more, and for this reason needs to be tailored to the specific individual. Self-care is:

> Whatever helps you through the day, know that you deserve to take those few minutes to prepare yourself.

- self-initiated
- regular, not just for emergencies
- flexible enough to respond to changing circumstances and needs
- caring for yourself beyond concerns of what others can 'see'
- looking after your mental and emotional needs, as well as your body's basic needs.

Self-care is *not* an emergency response to unexpected trauma. Rather, it is the regular care that allows you to be better equipped to manage that trauma, as well as giving you the ability to respond to the challenges of day-to-day living. While self-care is something that should always be maintained, you will also need to remain flexible enough to recognise when your self-care plan isn't working or when you need to take extra steps in response to a changing situation or trauma. It can take some time and experience to get right. (It is an ongoing journey for me and many of the other women I interviewed for this book.)

Looking after your body's needs

...

The most obvious element of self-care is basic physical care. Though this is logically something we should already be aware of, looking after our body's needs is one of the things we sometimes let slip when faced with high stress or trauma, and that can make it very hard to deal well with our situation. If we regularly and consciously attend to these needs, and remind ourselves in times of stress to keep on attending to them, we are less likely to burn out, or find ourselves dealing with major health problems.

Ask yourself: Am I drinking enough water? Do I have a decent diet? Am I getting adequate exercise and rest? All of these things will help you to survive and even thrive. No one is always on track with their health, but you will want to keep it in mind daily.

Get enough sleep for you. Drink plenty of water. Eat that apple. Take that walk. Hike, learn yoga, get involved in roller derby – whatever you need to do to get active. You can be more productive and less prone to burnout and illness when you look after your health. Plus, it just feels a whole lot better.

Water

Water is, of course, vital for our survival. Health authorities generally recommend 2 litres of water per day (8 x 8 ounce glasses, or half a gallon), but actual water requirements vary enormously depending on metabolism, climate conditions and stress levels. Staying hydrated should always be a priority, so make sure you have easy access to clean water (and be grateful for it, because many millions of people today don't) and strongly consider carrying a refillable water bottle with you in your bag or keeping one at your desk.

According to the World Health Organisation, a loss of body water of just 5% through dehydration can result in difficulty concentrating, headaches and sleepiness. At 6% you can begin to feel a tingling in your limbs. (It's something I've experienced while visiting Syrian refugee camps in Lebanon in summer, with very high temperatures inside the tents. I had to work hard to stay hydrated and avoid further problems.) A 7% loss of body water can lead to collapse, and a 10% loss is life-threatening.[4]

Sleep

There is a strong link between sleep problems and ill health, and even depression. It varies from individual to individual but it is generally recommended that adults get seven to nine hours of sleep per night, while seniors may need less, and children need considerably more.[5]

It can be hard to get enough sleep in times of stress – I know I have plenty of sleepless nights when my workload is intense – but keeping good sleep habits can help. If you are experiencing sleep problems, try to follow a fairly consistent sleep schedule, and avoid caffeine, sugary foods, chocolate, and screen time on computers or devices later in the evening. These things all contribute to wakefulness. Hot baths, herbal teas and a good book before bedtime can all help you to drop off. If you are having prolonged or severe sleep problems, speak to your doctor or trusted heath professional.

Exercise

Exercise is also vital for good health. Australia's Department of Health recommends the following:

- Be active most – preferably all – days of the week.
- Aim for a total of two and a half to five hours of moderate intensity physical activity, or one and a quarter to two and

a half hours of vigorous intensity physical activity (or an equivalent combination of the two) each week.

- Do muscle-strengthening activities at least two days per week.[6]

Staying active will help you become healthier and stronger. That will help you to look after yourself and others better.

Good diet

This isn't a cookbook or diet book, so I won't go into detail about dietary needs, but in summary, a poor diet can lead to fatigue, irritability, illness, increased risk of disease, burnout and a loss of productivity, not to mention loss of fun (to put it mildly). Diets that are high in sugar and processed foods are best avoided, and in my experience can lead me to 'yo-yo' in terms of energy, giving me a very temporary energy spike but leaving me ultimately more exhausted and less able to cope. Speak to a trusted health professional if you have any concerns about your diet, and in times of stress, try to avoid temporary fixes that will result in a sugar/caffeine crash later.

NOTE: Good health does not equal being thin. Active people come in all shapes and sizes. Get regular check-ups and always speak to a trusted doctor or health professional before making major changes to your diet or exercise regime, or if you have any concerns or unexplained pains.

Looking after your mental and emotional wellbeing

...

Self-care is not only about caring for your physical wellbeing. An equally important and sometimes more complicated aspect is caring for your mental and emotional wellbeing. Keep tabs on your mental health, emotional state and what helps you to cope and feel well, as well as what does not.

- Try to take note of your day-to-day emotional and mental state, and become attuned to what activities, work events or hobbies make you feel happy, stressed or upset, or confident vs disempowered.
- Make a list of things that make you feel good – a bath, a dinner with a friend, a walk, etc.
- Try to reduce exposure to circumstances that you know make you feel stressed, anxious, or unhappy. If it is not possible to reduce those stresses (for work reasons, for example) remind yourself that you will do something later that makes you feel better. Make concrete plans to do things (like those you listed above) that make you feel good.
- Try to be aware of changes in your mental or emotional state. Are you feeling more stressed than usual? Are you experiencing more negative thoughts? Have your sleep patterns or weight changed due to stress and anxiety, or depression and emotional fatigue? If so, try to get to the bottom of the possible root causes. Has something new occurred that is causing you distress? Can something be done to remove the cause?
- Life can be difficult at times, and sometimes it is not even possible to pinpoint the root cause of depression, anxiety or

emotional upset. Don't be hard on yourself if you feel down or like you can't cope. It happens to the best of us, and is a common part of being human. Remember, it *can* get better.

- Reach out for support from trusted friends, family, colleagues or mental health professionals. Do what you need for you.
- You should get to know what works for you so you can create your personal self-care plan. (We will go into some detail about what that can look like, below.)

Creating networks

• • •

Supporting others matters. So does having other people who can support you.

Consciously work on creating networks of friends and people who will challenge and support you. This is an extremely important factor for me and for many other women (see **Chapter 14: Stories of Survival**). If you see others going through what you are, struggling with the same pressures, or working as advocates in the same or similar spaces, reach out and offer *them* support. Humans are social animals, and most people need a certain amount of social contact for their wellbeing and enjoyment of life.

> Supporting others matters. So does having other people who can support you.

Make sure you don't cut out that part of your life when you get busy. Friendships and social connections are important for wellbeing and self-care. This can be particularly important for those who speak out, or those in occupations that are emotionally draining or involve exposure to vicarious trauma (see **Chapter 11**).

Learning self-care *for you*

...

Learning individualised self-care is important. This involves finding out what works for you personally – what helps you to unwind, and what helps you to feel good about yourself and rebalance your feelings about the world around you. Some work and advocacy environments involve regular exposure to trauma that can cause you to feel overwhelmed or depressed, particularly if it is triggering for you, and can make life seem unrelentingly dark. Regular self-care helps to keep things balanced, but it must be tailored to your own needs and interests. One size does *not* fit all.

Think about what gives you energy and makes you feel happy, beyond all the physical and mental health basics discussed above. Consider hobbies, sports and social occasions that have given you joy in the past. Do weekend team sports do it for you? How about hiking? Daily walks with a friend? Cosplay (costume play)? Whether it is being part of a re-enactment club complete with dress-ups, doing swing dancing or simply reading good books, make sure you prioritise and make time for the things that give you energy. These are the things that will help you to cope with the rest of life's challenges.

> Don't over-think it. If it works for you, gives you energy, and isn't hurting anyone, just do it.

Don't over-think it. If it works for you, gives you energy, and isn't hurting anyone, just do it. Try not to judge it. By helping yourself, you'll be more able to keep doing what you need to do or what you are passionate about, including helping others.

Women talk self-care

...

For me self-care is something different to short-term pleasure, it's about long term maintenance to ensure you can keep on going. To me, self-care is the realisation you are important and must ensure you can keep going. That means looking after your body, mind and home. You want to look after yourself because you have value and you can't let that belief go, no matter what anyone says online. Self-care is not only a radical act, it's also an act of healthy revenge. When I look after myself, I know I can keep working, keep talking and keep making change happen. Me being healthy is a brilliant act of revenge against those who don't want me continuing my work.

– Amy Gray, writer.

My meditation and yoga practices are gold to me. And I know I'm falling off the wagon of self-care when I 'don't have time' for either. You can always make ten minutes to meditate, anywhere, anytime, even if it means locking yourself in a bathroom with a baby on your lap.

– Amanda Palmer, artist, rock star, crowd-funding pioneer

The best self-care strategies are the ones that work for you, not necessarily anyone else. Mine change from time to time – getting blind drunk and/or eating a whole pizza is a legitimate response to some problems! But I also love baths, cute movies, long chats, cuddling my dog, and baking large quantities of delicious food for distribution.

– Karen Pickering, feminist organiser and educator

You always have to remember to take care of yourself first and foremost, because when you stop taking care of yourself you get out of balance and you really forget how to take care of others.[7]

– Jada Pinkett Smith, actor and director

Self-care checklist

Having a bad day? Feel like everything is harder than usual? Ask yourself these questions as part of your basic checklist:

Have I eaten in the past few hours? If not, your blood sugar level may be low. Signs include dizziness, headaches, tiredness, perspiration and even nausea. Try to eat something to normalise your blood sugar. High-sugar treats will likely result in a brief boost followed by another low, so try to eat something healthy and natural (preferably high in protein and low in artificial ingredients) that will stabilise you for longer.

Am I well hydrated? Signs of dehydration can include headaches, muscle aches, tiredness and more. Drink water regularly, and start *now*.

Have I had too much caffeine? Drinking more coffee, tea or energy drinks than usual can make you feel jittery, anxious and stressed. Eating, drinking some water and waiting for the jitteriness to pass may make you feel a whole lot better. If you regularly feel stressed, or you are experiencing a period of intense anxiety, consider cutting back the amount of caffeine you consume, or quitting entirely.

Have I underslept? If so, this can contribute to your feeling low or unable to cope. Try to prioritise sleep. If lack of sleep is a regular problem and you think you may have a sleeping disorder, see your doctor. If kids are causing your lack of sleep, ask for help from partners, friends or family to give you a break from time to time.

Have I taken a shower or bath today? When under stress, we can sometimes fall out of our usual routines. If you are feeling anxious and stressed, a bath can help relax you. If you feel down, a shower can be invigorating.

Have I been out of the house today? Fresh air and sunlight can have miraculous effects on wellbeing. If you haven't been outside for a while, get up and get out there. Even a short walk around the block can do wonders. Take that few minutes as some well-deserved time out.

Have I spoken to anyone lately? Social isolation has a direct correlation to bad physical and mental health. Even if it is speaking to someone at the corner store, or on the phone for a few minutes, make sure you reconnect regularly with others. Better yet, call a friend or trusted family member and organise to meet up.

Make no mistake – those who are working hardest to help others, those who are toiling to bring about positive change, those who are working to make a breakthrough in their field or to make the world safer, need to practise self-care to keep going. It is specifically the difficulty of caring for others, or facing discrimination, or challenging the status quo, or being exposed to harmful messages that you are worthless that makes self-care even more vital.

Whatever your contributions are or will be, without self-care you will risk burn out, and we don't want that, you don't want that, and those who rely on you or can benefit from your contribution don't want that.

Prioritise self-care in your life and see what you are capable of.

A Few Final Words

•••

You asked, so I wrote. (Well, maybe not you personally, but hundreds of other women and girls.) In this book I have done my best to distil the basics of speaking out and participating in public life, as I know it, and why it matters so much. The next step is yours.

I hope this handbook has inspired you or someone you love to speak out, and to do so with more confidence, after good-quality research and critical thinking, and with the support and self-care needed to keep going.

Speak out and keep on speaking out, whether it is through speeches, journalism, blogs, opinion pieces, teaching, storytelling, art, political action or all of the above. Find your way, and don't be silenced.

Your voice matters.

We need you.

x Tara

Endnotes

...

Chapter 1

1 This gendered dynamic further intersects with racism, ableism, homophobia, classism and other forms of dominance, oppression and discrimination, so that women of colour, to take one example, are less often heard in the public sphere than those who are white. Likewise, those who are not wealthy compared with those who are.

2 www.dailymail.co.uk/sciencetech/article-2281891/Women-really-talk-men-13-000-words-day-precise.html#ixzz3nIEDUT2W

3 J. Michael Bowers, Miguel Perez-Poucholen, N. Shalon Edwards, and Margaret M. McCarthy, 'Foxp2 mediates sex differences in ultrasonic vocalization by rat pups and directs order of maternal retrieval', *The Journal of Neuroscience*, 33(8):3276:3283, 20 February 2013

4 Simon E. Fisher, Faraneh Vargha-Khadem, Kate E. Watkins, Anthony P. Monaco and Marcus E. Pembrey, 'Localisation of a gene implicated in a severe speech and language disorder', *Nature Genetics* 18, 168-170, 1998

5 www.bbc.com/future/story/20131112-do-women-talk-more-than-men

6 Deborah James and Janice Drakich, 'Understanding gender differences in amount of talk', in Deborah Tannen (ed.), *Gender and Conversational Interaction*, Oxford University Press, New York/Oxford, 1993

7 www.linguistik-online.com/1_00/KUNSMANN.HTM

8 www.salon.com/2014/04/28/the_problem_with_saying_the_media_has_a_%E2%80%9Cwoman_problem%E2%80%9D

9 Plutarch, *Morals*, 381ef, quoted in www.arch.uoa.gr/fileadmin/arch.uoa.gr/uploads/images/evy_johanne_haland/mr_2012.pdf

10 Both Bible quotes from New International Version, Biblica, 2011

11 www.derbyshireheritage.co.uk/Menu/Curiosities/The-Quiet-Woman-Earl-Sterndale.php

12 www.smh.com.au/lifestyle/life/do-you-know-what-your-daughters-doing-tonight-20110629-1gqda

13 www.slate.com/articles/double_x/doublex/2013/10/sexual_assault_and_drinking_teach_women_the_connection.html

14 www.oxfordmail.co.uk/news/11431450.Judge_in_rape_trail_
    warning_____Conviction_rates_will_not_improve_until_women_
    stop_drinking_so_heavily___/

15 www.vocativ.com/news/278919/pregnancy-alcohol-use-cdc/

16 Andra Medea and Kathleen Thompson, *Against Rape,* Farrar, Straus
    and Giroux, New York, 1974, p. 59

17 www.ourwatch.org.au/Understanding-Violence/Facts-and-figures

18 www.theguardian.com/theguardian/from-the-archive-blog/2012/
    nov/15/el-vino-women-ban-fleet-street-1982

19 www.abc.net.au/news/2014-07-31/women-in-turkey-defy-call-not-to-
    laugh-in-public/5637742

20 bianet.org/english/women/166434-bulent-arinc-be-silent-as-a-woman

21 instagram.com/p/bhsfdOt7HZ/

22 www.youtube.com/watch?v=URWXkPDwG0g

23 twitter.com/SenatorWong/status/630611154574782464

24 www.theaustralian.com.au/national-affairs/peta-credlin-rallies-
    liberal-women-members/news-story/4b1c00401dfe1073c3f07e9
    8f4482086

25 www.huffingtonpost.com.au/entry/hillary-clinton-gun-control_562a5
    3fee4b0ec0a38942fd1?section=australia&adsSiteOverride=au

26 asq.sagepub.com/content/early/2012/02/28/0001839212439994.
    abstract

27 www.theguardian.com/australia-news/2015/sep/17/northern-
    territory-minister-who-told-female-mp-he-felt-like-slapping-her-says-
    it-was-a-metaphor

28 www.smh.com.au/sport/the-fitz-files/is-that-a-scandal-i-hear-
    brewing--it-must-be-time-for-another-nrl-season-20150227-13qjzg.
    html#ixzz3mX7ClQx5

29 www.jstor.org/stable/10.1525/si.1984.7.1.87?seq=1#page_scan_tab_
    contents (abstract)

30 Carole Edelsky, 'Who's got the floor?', in Deborah Tannen (ed.),
    Gender and Conversational Interaction, Oxford University Press,
    New York/Oxford, 1993

31 www.interruptions.net/literature/Rhoades-FM01.pdf

32 Deborah Tannen, *You Just Don't Understand: Women and Men in
    Conversation*, William Morrow, New York, 1990, p. 76

33 MUST GET PERMISSION www.law.harvard.edu/students/
    experiences/ExecutiveSummary.pdf; the study found that 'Women
    consistently volunteered to speak less often and made up a
    significantly smaller percentage of frequent talkers, those students

who speak three or more times in one class. Although the monitored classes were on average 45% female, women made 39% of the 7,831 total comments in our sample. This disparity primarily reflects a gender difference in student volunteered comments. A male student was 50% more likely to speak voluntarily at least once during a class meeting than was a female student.'

34 *Who Makes the News?* (2010), GMMP Report – Global Media Monitoring Project 2010, September, Annex 3, National Results, p. 94

35 ibid.

36 andrewwhitby.com/2013/11/11/abc-qanda-gender/

37 Ray Martin and Shaun Brown, 'ABC Editorial Review no. 6: Content, conduct and panel composition of the *Q&A* program (February–June 2015)', December 2015, pp. 102-104; see also www.theguardian.com/media/2015/dec/17/abcs-qa-program-should-give-women-proper-representation-says-report http://about.abc.net.au/wp-content/uploads/2015/12/ABCEditorialReview6.pdf

38 www.smh.com.au/business/media-and-marketing/silence-is-golden-for-women-in-radio-20140710-zt30h.html#ixzz3mXGbZjmJ

39 www.abc.net.au/news/2014-03-14/ford-male-privilege-extends-beyond-the-airwaves/5321558

40 thehoopla.com.au/women-radio-dial/

41 Chrys Stevenson, 'The blokeyness index: blokes win the gender war in Australia's 4th estate', *King's Tribune*, 6 December 2012, pp. 8–13

42 www.theguardian.com/lifeandstyle/2011/dec/04/why-british-public-life-dominated-men

43 www.4thestate.net/female-voices-in-media-infographic/

44 www.bunchecenter.ucla.edu/wp-content/uploads/2014/02/2014-Hollywood-Diversity-Report-2-12-14.pdf

45 www.nytimes.com/2015/11/22/magazine/the-women-of-hollywood-speak-out.html?smid=tw-nytmag&smtyp=cur&_r=0

46 womenintvfilm.sdsu.edu/files/2014_Celluloid_Ceiling_Report.pdf

47 annenberg.usc.edu/pages/~/media/MDSCI/Inequality%20in%20700%20Popular%20Films%208215%20Final%20for%20Posting.ashx

48 screencrush.com/star-wars-diversity-casting/

49 Rebecca Solnit, *Men Explain Things to Me*, Haymarket Books, USA, 2014

Chapter 2

1 www.theguardian.com/books/2013/sep/27/author-david-gilmour-female-writers

2   www.unwomen.org/en/what-we-do/leadership-and-political-
    participation/facts-and-figures#sthash.n3fiZryu.dpuf

3   www.theguardian.com/artanddesign/2010/jan/17/germaine-greer-
    elles-pompidou

4   Repucom, 'Media coverage and the economic value of women's sport
    in Australia', corporate briefing paper (not publicly available). From
    the document:
    Myth 1: Dedicated coverage of women's sport is decreasing. When
    compared to previous research in 2008, the volume of television
    event coverage dedicated to women's sport remains stable. Despite
    the addition of male dominated channels such as Fox Footy, women's
    sport accounts for 7% of all television event coverage on Australian
    television. 'Repucom estimates that the Australian sports sponsorship
    market is worth around $780m, of which only 8% is attributable to
    women's sport. Women's sport presents an underutilised opportunity
    for corporate Australia.'

5   Email to Tara Moss

6   www.smithsonianmag.com/smart-news/central-park-has-no-statues-
    real-women-180955973/?no-ist

7   link.springer.com/article/10.1007/s10755-014-9313-4

8   news.ncsu.edu/2014/12/macnell-gender-2014/

9   www.pnas.org/content/109/41/16474.abstract

10 www.womensagenda.com.au/talking-about/editors-agenda/item/6761-
    another-study-proving-gender-bias-exists-another-reason-to-
    continue-our-effort-to-change-it

11 www.pnas.org/content/112/43/13201.full.pdf

12 www.abs.gov.au/AUSSTATS/abs@.nsf/
    Lookup/4102.0Main+Features20Sep+2012

13 www.newappsblog.com/2012/09/call-to-action-and-a-petition-in-
    support-of-the-gendered-conference-campaign-revised.html

14 news.nationalpost.com/news/philosophy-gender-war-sparked-by-call-
    for-larger-role-for-women

15 The 2015 Turnbull cabinet is 100% white and 85.7% are of
    predominantly Anglo-Celtic heritage. There is an Aboriginal member
    and a member with Aboriginal ancestry in the *ministry* but neither
    are in the *cabinet*; 16 of 21 cabinet members (76.1%) are Australian
    born of primarily Anglo-Celtic heritage; one is British born; one is
    Nigerian born of British parents; one is Australian born of Greek
    descent; one is Australian born of Polish/Jewish descent; one is
    Belgian born (German-speaking Belgium)

16 twitter.com/utopiana/status/645482434503446530
17 www.abc.net.au/news/2013-09-17/ita-buttrose-criticises-lack-of-
    women-in-cabinet/4961704
18 www.abc.net.au/am/content/2013/s3850120.htm
19 startsatsixty.com.au/current-affairs/news/see-why-this-list-of-
    canadas-amazingly-diverse-cabinet-is-going-viral-and-how-australia-
    compares; www.cbc.ca/news/politics/full-list-of-justin-trudeau-s-
    cabinet-1.3300699
20 freedomhouse.org/blog/exclusion-women-peace-negotiations#.
    Ved3J7Rqlvd

Chapter 3

1   www.dailylife.com.au/news-and-views/lisa-wilkinson-and-annabel-
    crabb-lament-viewer-obsession-with-female-tv-journalists-
    appearance-20131028-2wbge.html
2   Curiously the tome was published without a date (in the edition I
    have, anyway) but seems to have first been published in 1958.
3   www.youtube.com/watch?v=WO4tIrjBDkk
4   www.youtube.com/watch?v=D95HL51HlVI
5   www.youtube.com/watch?v=5meC4Z61qGg
6   languagelog.ldc.upenn.edu/nll/?p=3626&utm_
    source=twitterfeed&utm_medium=twitter
7   www.abc.net.au/correspondents/content/2015/s4171748.htm
8   www.youtube.com/watch?t=133&v=4iyJmpxtZDE
9   www.youtube.com/watch?v=txSSO4VglMI
10 languagelog.ldc.upenn.edu/nll/?p=17496
11 www.youtube.com/watch?t=133&v=4iyJmpxtZDE
12 www.ncbi.nlm.nih.gov/pmc/articles/PMC4037169
13 languagelog.ldc.upenn.edu/nll/?p=3226
14 info.noldus.com/throwing-shade-the-science-of-rbf
15 www.independent.co.uk/life-style/fashion/news/scientists-have-
    discovered-what-causes-resting-bitch-face-a6850441.html
16 www.theguardian.com/commentisfree/2015/jul/24/vocal-fry-strong-
    female-voice
17 nymag.com/thecut/2015/07/can-we-just-like-get-over-the-way-
    women-talk.html?mid=twitter_nymag#
18 www.newstatesman.com/world-view/2013/09/five-reasons-tony-
    abbott-shouldnt-be-womens-minister
19 www.voicecoach.net/lucy.php
20 www.voicecoach.net/store.php

21 www.nytimes.com/2015/11/22/magazine/the-women-of-hollywood-speak-out.html?smid=tw-nytmag&smtyp=cur&_r=0

Chapter 4

1 www.womensagenda.com.au/talking-about/item/6380-a-collection-of-hints-on-how-to-do-public-speaking

Chapter 5

1 Hélène Cixous, *Three Steps on the Ladder of Writing* (trans. Sarah Cornell and Susan Seller), Columbia University Press, New York, 1984, p.9

2 dangerousminds.net/comments/ernest_hemingway_and_the_six-word_short_story

3 The actual source of this story is debated. *Quote Investigator* suggests possible sources for the story may be early advertisements from 1906 onwards; newspaper stories, the first from 1910; or even an essay on creative writing by William R. Kane from 1917

4 Ernest Hemingway, *Selected Letters, 1917–61*, (ed. Carlos Baker), Scribner, London, 1981, p. 594.

5 blog.bufferapp.com/optimal-length-social-media

6 medium.com/data-lab/the-optimal-post-is-7-minutes-74b9f41509b#.4qui91a22

7 taramoss.com/manus-island-insiders-report

8 Stephen King, *On Writing*, Scribner, New York, 2000, p. 56

9 valenciacollege.edu/wp/cssc/documents/ElementsofPersuasive.pdf

10 Stephen King, *On Writing*, Scribner, New York, 2000, p. 117–118

Chapter 6

1 www.criticalthinking.org/files/Concepts_Tools.pdf

2 theness.com/neurologicablog/index.php/how-to-argue/

3 web.archive.org/web/20090114165606/www.chips.navy.mil/archives/86_jul/interview.html

4 www.news.com.au/lifestyle/real-life/mark-ruffalo-on-the-i-am-not-a-feminist-internet-phenomenon/story-fnu2q5nu-1227372981280

5 www.womenyoushouldknow.net/response-to-i-am-not-a-feminist-libby-anne-bruce-wrote-it-mark-ruffalo-shared-it-and-its-awesome/

6 quoteinvestigator.com/2015/06/01/defend-say/

7 www.copyright.org.au/acc_prod/ACC/Information_Sheets/Fair_Dealing__What_Can_I_Use_Without_Permission.aspx

8 www.copyright.org.au/ACC_Prod/ACC/Information_Sheets/
Quotes___Extracts.aspx?WebsiteKey=8a471e74-3f78-4994-9023-
316f0ecef4ef

Chapter 7

1 www.unwomen.org/en/what-we-do/ending-violence-against-women/
prevention
2 www.theadvertiser.com/story/life/people/2015/11/30/acadiana-
barista-helps-men-discover-inner-strength/76450338/
3 www.cbsnews.com/news/san-bernardino-shooting-american-women-
increasingly-interested-in-terrorism/
4 suite.io/bailey-poland/6s1g2mv
5 www.sbs.com.au/comedy/article/2015/10/20/david-jones-risk-losing-
racist-idiot-market
6 www.nbcnews.com/politics/2016-election/donald-trump-resumes-
fight-against-fox-news-anchor-megyn-kelly-n541921?cid=sm_fb
7 time.com/4198737/donald-trump-megyn-kelly-sexism/

Chapter 8

1 www.onlinecollege.org/2010/02/16/50-famously-successful-people-
who-failed-at-first/
2 thoughtcatalog.com/rachel-hodin/2013/10/35-famous-people-who-
were-painfully-rejected-before-making-it-big/
3 www.onlinecollege.org/2010/02/16/50-famously-successful-people-
who-failed-at-first/
4 www.historyofaboriginalsydney.edu.au/south-coastal/meeting-my-
auntie-first-time-pamela-young
5 www.wsj.com/articles/how-to-take-criticism-well-1403046866
6 books.google.com.au/books?id=EjL9qyGmJF4C&pg=PA31&redir_
esc=y#v=onepage&q&f=false

Chapter 9

1 www.theguardian.com/world/2013/jun/13/julia-gillard-howard-sattler-
interview
2 www.youtube.com/watch?v=na6xzMXNjWA
3 *University of Alberta Sexual Assault Centre* (undated), 'Triggers and
Flashbacks', www.ualberta.ca/~uasac/Triggers.htm
4 *Empowered Together* (2015), 'Flashbacks', www.empoweredtogether.
com.au/support_flashbacks/#

Chapter 10

1   As the writer passed away recently and the article can no longer be accessed online, I have decided not to name him or his publisher here.

2   twitter.com/bairdjulia/status/477370073812705280

Chapter 11

1   www.fullstopfoundation.org.au

2   www.who.int/mediacentre/factsheets/fs239/en

Chapter 12

1   www.norton.com/au/survey-women

2   www.standard.co.uk/news/london/caroline-criadoperez-how-i-won-my-banknote-battle-and-defied-rape-threat-trolls-a3123956.html

3   Sample size: 1,053 18+ year old women and an equal number of men. Typical margin of statistical error +/- 3.0%. For more information see: www.norton.com/au/survey-women

4   www.dailylife.com.au/news-and-views/dl-opinion/tweet-creep-20160309-gnefnb.html

5   www.lawstuff.org.au/nsw_law/topics/bullying/cyber-bullying

6   www.endrevengeporn.org/revenge-porn-laws

7   www.dailylife.com.au/dl-people/celebrity-news/labor-mp-tim-watts-introduces-revenge-porn-bill-says-blaming-women-for-the-crime-is-wrong-20151012-gk76zj.html

8   au.norton.com/cybercrime-landing

9   www.theaustralian.com.au/life/weekend-australian-magazine/are-kids- safe-online-answer-is-theyre-only-as-safe-as-you-make-them/news-story/d256712c9e273c00b07aacf15b8a4b25

10 sydney.edu.au/law/slr/slr_35/slr35_1/04_Crofts_Lee.pdf

11 www.lawstuff.org.au/wa_law/topics/privacy

12 crashoverridenetwork.tumblr.com/post/108387569412/preventing-doxing

Chapter 13

1   twitter.com/rubyhamad/status/659669955231612928

2   twitter.com/JohnCleese/status/711348180810502145

3   www.facebook.com/georgehtakei/photos/a.737221629640626.1073741825.205344452828349/1386491291380320/?type=3&theater

Chapter 14

1 www.abc.net.au/news/2014-10-23/luke-batty-inquest-father-was-100-per-cent-bad/5835800

2 http://carlyfindlay.blogspot.com.au/2013/12/how-to-win-internet-or-how-to-defend.html

3 mariamveiszadeh.com/2015/11/23/death-threats-in-the-virtual-world-meant-i-had-to-worry-about-my-safety-in-the-real-one/

Chapter 15

1 www.iwpr.org/initiatives/pay-equity-and-discrimination

2 newrepublic.com/article/121530/women-color-make-far-less-78-cents-mans-dollar

3 Audre Lorde, *A Burst of Light: Essays,* Firebrand Books, New York, 1988, p. 131

4 www.who.int/water_sanitation_health/dwq/nutwaterrequir.pdf

5 sleepfoundation.org/video-library

6 www.health.gov.au/internet/main/publishing.nsf/content/health-pubhlth-strateg-phys-act-guidelines#apaadult

7 on.aol.com/video/red-table-talks--jada-pinkett-smith--willow-smith-talk-love--family-517362771

About the author

A dual Canadian/Australian citizen, Tara Moss is the bestselling
author of eleven books of fiction and non-fiction published in
nineteen countries, a journalist, doctoral candidate at the University
of Sydney, public speaker and outspoken advocate for children's
rights and women's rights. She is UNICEF Australia's National
Ambassador for Child Survival, Patron for the Full Stop Foundation
for ending rape and domestic violence and an ambassador for Our
Watch. She was Norton's 2015 Family Ambassador for child e-safety
and cyberbullying. In 2015 she received an Edna Ryan award for
making a feminist difference, inciting others to challenge the status
quo. Tara currently lives in New South Wales with her husband and
daughter. Visit her at taramoss.com